C000245476

THE SURVEY OF CORNWALL

THE
SVRVEY OF
CORNWALL.

*Written by Richard Carew
of Antonie, Esquire.*

First printed at London by S.S. for Iohn Iaggard,
and were to be fold near Temple Bar
at the fign of the Hand and Star
1602

Now reiffued in Cornwall by Tamar Books
Redruth
2000

Published 2000 by Tamar Books, an imprint of Tor Mark Press,
PO Box 4, Redruth, Cornwall TR16 5XY
© 2000 Tor Mark Press

ISBN 0-85025-389-6

The portrait of the author on the cover is reproduced by kind permission
of The Royal Institution of Cornwall.

Printed in Great Britain by R Booth (Troutbeck Press), Mabe, Cornwall

Introduction

In Cornwall we are truly fortunate that the earliest book devoted to the county is a minor masterpiece of Elizabethan prose. What is more, although an extraordinary number of titles about Cornwall have been produced in the four centuries since its publication, many people would argue that it remains the most important ever written about the county.

Here in Carew's *Survey of Cornwall* is a unique picture of the everyday life of Cornish people as they were 400 years ago, expressed in wonderfully robust language and with unforgettable originality, by an author who is always ready to reveal his own personality and passions – which is part of the attraction of his book. He enters into great detail about such topics as seine-fishing, mining techniques, feast days, church ales, archery and the two versions of hurling (one of which is clearly the predecessor of today's codes of rugby) and he tells us about individual people – some poor folk as well as the gentry.

The *Survey* should consequently be of great interest to everyone who lives in Cornwall or loves the county, though it was published probably early in what we call 1603 (under the old calendar then in use it was still 1602, hence the title page date) while Queen Elizabeth lay dying and *King Lear* and *Macbeth* had not yet been thought of. It is a long time ago and the archaic language may seem a barrier to some readers, but the trick is to persist, and if you don't understand a detail, ignore it and read on! The same applies to Carew's digressions into heraldry or (unreliable) history – just skip if you want to, and you will soon arrive at more interesting fare.

Because we want this edition to be accessible to everyone, it is published with modern type, modern punctuation and modern spelling – except for place-names where the old spelling is interesting. Occasional explanations or translations of foreign phrases are given in square brackets rather than footnotes, and this introduction has been deliberately kept short and does not pretend to academic standards.

The text is the complete text of the 1602/3 edition except for some medieval parish tax returns (in Latin) which Carew had found and thought worth reprinting, but which we hope you will not miss. In the most recent previous edition, that edited by F E Halliday (published by Andrew Melrose in 1953) there were many gaps, often omitting material of interest to people in Cornwall but less so to outsiders. The Halliday edition does have the advantage of a good and extensive introduction and also contains Carew's lesser known works: it is available through public libraries, or in antiquarian bookshops.

The Author

Richard Carew of Antony (a characteristically Cornish way of distinguishing himself from the numerous other West Country branches of that famous family) was born in 1555, just nine years before Shakespeare. He was educated at Oxford, becoming a 'gentleman-commoner' at the age of 11. In Elizabethan days the gentry used Oxbridge more like a school than a university, and as was then normal Carew moved on at the age of 19 to one of the London Inns of Court (the Middle Temple) for his higher education. At Oxford he was a contemporary of Sir Philip Sidney, with whom, as he is understandably proud to tell us, he debated before an invited audience of the greatest men in the kingdom – in schoolboy Latin. One hopes the noble Earls of Leicester and Warwick could follow the arguments, and that Oxford cellars were as well stocked then as nowadays, so that at least they had a good evening afterwards.

Carew's studious habits at Oxford and the Middle Temple brought him into contact with the leading lights of both the literary and antiquarian worlds. He wrote poetry, which in those days was mainly circulated in manuscript between like-minded people. By this means Carew knew of and admired Shakespeare as a poet; probably he never saw a Shakespeare play – and they did not move in the same social circles. Carew was also part of a group which began to meet at the house of Sir Robert Cotton, and included William Camden (another Oxford contemporary) and John Stow. This group became the Society of Antiquaries, and was a key element in the development of historical studies in England – though as the *Survey* itself demonstrates, the study of British history and of etymology were both in their very early days in Tudor England!

But Richard Carew's interests extended beyond libraries. As a member of the Cornish gentry he was pleased to take a full part in the county administration, which at that time was almost entirely devolved from the Queen to the gentry. Carew fulfilled such roles as Sheriff of the county, MP for Saltash and later Mitchell, and in 1586 he became a Deputy Lieutenant of the county with 500 men under his command. He was responsible for the defence of the Cawsand area – a post he continued to hold at the time of the Armada, for which he cannot be envied!

In 1577 Richard Carew married 14-year-old Juliana Arundell of Trerice. He tells us of a proverb, that 'all Cornish gentlemen are cousins', and he is himself an extreme example of this. Either by birth or marriage he seems to be related to every 'county' family before or since! And this network extended well beyond the Tamar, as did his landholdings.

The *Survey* was originally written for circulation among the gentry, rather like poetry, and they would have understood the Classical references. The numerous family genealogies were doubtless of interest to the marriage arrangers among them! Carew also has many of the social and very English prejudices of his class; for example, he writes patronisingly of Cornish tinners:

> If you did see how aptly they cast the ground for conveying the water, by compassings and turnings to shun such hills and valleys as [hinder] them by their too much height or lowness, you would wonder how so great skill could couch in so base a cabin as their (otherwise) thickclouded brains.

Another subject on which he is weak is the Cornish language, which was in the later stages of its decline as he wrote. Although it is claimed for him that he had learned many languages, Cornish seems not to have been one of them. The Cornish he quotes is badly flawed and often mistranslated; perhaps he had heard examples at the supper table from his friends in the western parts of Cornwall, where the language was still spoken, rather than from mother-tongue speakers.

This defect is uncharacteristic. The great achievement of the *Survey of Cornwall*, especially compared with topographical works from the following three centuries, is that Carew writes to a large extent from personal observation, rather than reworking earlier authors' materials, and he has decided for himself what he thinks is worth noting. He had ridden about the county on his administrative duties, seen for himself what was happening and been able to get detailed information from his colleagues, for example on mining techniques from Sir Francis Godolphin.

To me it is the combination of this direct evidence, and the way he reveals his own personality, which makes his book so fascinating.

Paul White, June 2000

To the Honourable, Sir Walter Raleigh, Knight,

Lord Warden of the Stannaries, Lieutenant General of Cornwall, &c.

This mine ill-husbanded Survey, long since begun, a great while discontinued, lately reviewed, and now hastily finished, appealeth to your Lordship's direction, whether it should pass; to your correction, if it do pass; and to your protection, when it is passed. Neither unduly: for the same intreateth of the Province and persons, over whose bodies and estates you carry a large, both martial and civil command, by your authority, but in whose hearts and loves you possess a far greater interest by your kindness. Your ears and mouth have ever been open to hear and deliver our grievances, and your feet and hands ready to go and work their redress, and that, not only always as a magistrate, of yourself, but also very often as a suitor and solicitor to others of the highest place. Wherefore I, as one of the common beholden, present this token of my private gratitude. It is duty, and not presumption, that hath drawn me to the offering; and it must be favour, and not desert, that shall move your Lordship to the acceptance: and so I take humble leave, resting no less willing to serve you, than under you.

Your Lordship's poor kinsman,

Richard Carew of
Antonie.

To the Reader

When I first composed this treatise, not minding that it should be published in print, I caused only certain written copies to be given to some of my friends, and put Prosopopeia into the book's mouth. But since that time, Master Camden's often mentioning this work, and my friends' persuasions, have caused my determination to alter, and to embrace a pleasing hope that charity and good construction resteth now generally in all readers. Albeit, I well know how *Opere in vario*, no less than *in longo, fas est obrepere somnum* [In a varied/complex work, no less than in a long one, sleep may steal up on you]. And I acknowledge this playing work to come so far short of satisfying even myself (though *suus cuique placet partus* [everyone likes their own child]), as I have little reason to expect the applause of any other.

Besides, the state of our country hath undergone so many alterations since I first began these scribblings, that in the reviewing I was driven either likewise to vary my report or else to speak against my knowledge. And no marvel, for each succeeding time addeth or reaveth goods and evils according to the occasions which itself produceth; rather a wonder it were that in the ceaseless revolution of the universe any parcel should retain a steadfast constitution. Reckon therefore (I pray you) that this treatise plotteth down Cornwall as it now standeth, for the particulars, and will continue, for the general. Mine eulogies proceed no less from the sincerity of a witness, than the affection of a friend; and therefore I hope that where my tongue hath been good no man's eye will be evil, and that each well-minded reader will wish a merry passage to this my rather fancy-sporting than gain-seeking voyage.

Farewell.

The Prosopopeia to the Book

I crave not courteous aid of friends
    To blaze my praise in verse;
Nor, proud of vaunt, mine author's names
    In catalogue rehearse.

I of no willing wrong complain,
    Which force or stealth hath wrought,
No fruit I promise from the tree
    Which forth this blooth hath brought.

I curry not with smoothing terms,
    Ne yet rude threats I blast:
I seek no patron for my faults,
    I plead no needless haste.

But as a child of feeble force,
    I keep my father's home,
And, bashful at each stranger's sight,
    Dare not abroad to roam,

Save to his kin of nearest blood,
    Or friends of dearest price,
Who, for his sake, not my desert,
    With welcome me entice.

The First Book

Cornwall, the farthest shire of England westwards, hath her name by divers authors diversely derived. Some (as our own chroniclers) draw it from Corineus, cousin to Brute, the first conqueror of this island, who wrestling at Plymmouth (as they say) with a mighty giant called Gogmagog, threw him over cliff, brake his neck, and received the gift of that country in reward for his prowess; some, as Cerealis (no less mistaken perhaps in that than in his measures), from *Cornu Galliae*, a horn or corner of France, where against nature hath placed it; and some from *Cornu Walliae*, which (in my conjecture) carrieth greatest likelihood of truth.

For what time the Saxons, after many bloody invasions as pirates, began at last to plant their dwellings, and to take root in this island as conquerors, the Britons, by them supplanted, were driven to seek their safeguard in the waste moors, craggy mountains, and wild forests of Wales and Cornwall, where the country's barrenness barred their pursuers from victuals, and the dangerousness of the passages laid them open to privy invasions. Such as had in this sort withdrawn themselves, the Saxons termed Welshmen, by interpretation strangers for so they were to them, as they to the country: and their place of abode they called Welshland, since turned to Wales, even as by the same reason they give still the same name to Italy. Now, Cornwall being cast out into the sea, with the shape of a horn, borrowed the one part of her name from her fashion, as Matthew of Westminster testifieth, and the other from her inhabitants, both which conjoined make Cornuwalliae, and contrived, Cornwall: in which sense the Cornish people call it Kernow, derived likewise from Kerne, a horn. Neither needeth this composition to be accounted any way uncouth, seeing the same is made familiar unto us by the like in other countries as of Herbipolis in Germany, Lombardy in Italy, Paleocastrum in Crete, and Neoportus in Carniola: all which, with many others, are likewise compacted of double languages.

This ill-halsening [ominous] horny name hath (as Corneto in Italy) opened a gap to the scoffs of many who, not knowing their own present condition, or at least their future destiny, can be contented to draw an odious mirth from a public infamy. But seeing the wisest enditer hath directed the pen of his holiest writers to use this term, not only in a good meaning but also in a significant sense, and to sanctify the thing itself in sundry parts of his service, such jesters' dishonest indiscretion is rather charitably to be pitied, than their exception either angerly [with pain] to be grieved at, or seriously to be confuted.

I am not ignorant how sorely the whole story of Brute is shaken by some of our late writers, and how stiffly supported by other some: as also, that this wrestling pull between Corineus and Gogmagog is reported to have befallen at Dover. For mine own part, though I reverence antiquity, and reckon it a kind of wrong to exact an overstrict reason for all that which upon credit she delivereth, yet I rather incline to their side who would warrant her authority by apparent verity. Notwithstanding, in this question I will not take on me the person of either judge or stickler [the referee in a wrestling match], and therefore, if there be any so plunged in the common flood as they will gripe fast what they have once caught hold on, let them sport themselves with these conjectures upon which my averment in behalf of Plymmouth is grounded. The place where Brute is said to have first landed was Totnes in Cornwall, and therefore this wrestling likely to have chanced there sooner than elsewhere. The province bestowed on Corineus for this exploit was Cornwall. It may then be presumed that he received in reward the place where he made proof of his worth, and whose prince (for so with others I take Gogmagog to have been) he had conquered, even as Cyrus recompensed Zopirus with the city Babylon, which his policy had recovered. Again, the activity of Devon and Cornish men in this faculty of wrestling, beyond those of other shires, doth seem to derive them a special pedigree from that grand wrestler Corineus. Moreover, upon the Hoe at Plymmouth there is cut in the ground the portraiture of two men, the one bigger, the other lesser, with clubs in their hands, (whom they term Gog-magog) and (as I have learned) it is renewed by order of the townsmen when cause requireth, which should infer the same to be a monument of some moment. And lastly, the place, having a steep cliff adjoining, affordeth an opportunity to the fact. But of this too much.

Cornwall is situated (as most men account) in the latitude of fifty degrees and thirty minutes, and in the longitude of six. The shire extendeth in length to about seventy miles: the breadth, as almost nowhere equal, so in the largest place it passeth not thirty, in the middle twenty, and in the narrowest of the west part three. The whole compass may hereby be conjectured.

It bordereth on the east with Devon, divided therefrom in most places by the River Tamer, which springing near the North Sea at Hartland in Devon, runneth through Plymmouth Haven into the South. For the rest, the main ocean sundereth the same, on the north from Ireland, on the west from the Islands of Scilley, and on the south from little Britaine. These borders, now thus straitened, did once extend so wide as that they ennobled their enclosed territory with the title of a kingdom. Polidore Virgil alloteth it the fourth part of the whole island, and the ancient chroniclers report that Brute landed at Totnes in Cornwall, a town now seated in the midst of Devon. Moreover, until Athelstan's time the Cornishmen bare equal sway in Excester with the English, for he it was who hemmed them within their present limits. Lastly, the encroaching sea hath ravined from it the whole country of Lionnesse, together with divers other parcels of no little circuit, and that such a Lionnesse there was these proofs are yet remaining. The space between the land's end and the Isles of Scilley, being about thirty miles, to this day retaineth the name, in Cornish *Lethowsow*, and carrieth continually an equal depth of forty or sixty fathom (a thing not usual in the sea's proper dominion) save that about the midway there lieth a rock which at low water discovereth his head. They term it the Gulfe, suiting thereby the other name of Scilla. Fishermen also casting their hooks thereabouts have drawn up pieces of doors and windows. Moreover, the ancient name of Saint Michael's Mount was *Cara clowse in Cowse*, in English, The Hoare Rocke in the Wood, which now is at every flood encompassed by the sea, and yet at some low ebbs roots of mighty trees are descried in the sands about it. The like overflowing hath happened in Plymmouth Haven and divers other places.

In this situation, though nature hath shouldered out Cornwall into the farthest part of the realm, and so besieged it with the ocean, that, as a demi-island in an island, the inhabitants find but one way of issue by land, yet hath she in some good measure countervailed such disadvantage through placing it both near unto and in the trade way between Wales, Ireland, Spain, France, and Netherland. The nearness helpeth them with a shorter cut, less peril, and meaner charge, to vent forth and make return of those commodities which their own or either of those countries do afford; the lying in the way bringeth foreign ships to claim succour at their harbours, when either outward or homeward bound they are checked by an east, south, or south-east wind; and where the horse walloweth, some hairs will still remain. Neither is it to be passed over without regard that these remote quarters lie not so open to the invasions of foreign enemies, or spoils of civil tumults, as other more inward parts of the realm, which being seated nearer the heart, are sooner sought and easier ransacked in such troublesome times; or if the country's long naked sides offer occasion of landing to any adverse shipping, her forementioned inward natural strength, increased by so many lanes and enclosures, straiteneth the same to a preying only upon the outward skirts by some petty fleets; for the danger of farther piercing will require the protection of a greater force for execution than can there be countervailed with the benefit of any booty or conquest, were they sure to prevail. And if to be free from a damage may pass for a commodity, I can add that the far distance of this county from the Court hath heretofore afforded it a *supersedeas* [exemption] from takers and purveyors [purveyors could requisition provisions to support the Court, as the monarch 'progressed' round the country]; for if they should fetch any provision from thence, well it might be masked with the vizard of her Highness' prerogative, but the same would very slenderly turn to the benefit of her Majesty's housekeeping: for the foulness and uneasiness of the ways, the little mould of Cornish cattle, and the great expense of driving them, would defalk [subtract] as much from the just price to the Queen at the delivering as it did from the owners at the taking. Besides that, her Highness' shipping should therethrough be defrauded of often supplies, which these parts afford unto them.

Upon which reasons, some of the purveyors' attempts, heretofore through the suit of the country, the solicitation of Sir Richard Greinvile, the credit of the Lord Warden, and the graciousness of our Sovereign, were revoked and suppressed, and the same under her Highness' privy seal confirmed. Notwithstanding, when her Majesty made her pleasure afterward known, that she would have a general contribution from every shire, for redeeming this exemption, Cornwall, opposing duty against reason, or rather accounting duty a reason sufficient, yielded to undergo a proportionable rate of the burden. So they compounded to furnish ten oxen after Michaelmas for thirty pound price: to which, by another agreement with the officers, they should add forty marks of their own. Upon half a year's warning either party might repent the bargain. This held for a while; but within a short space, either the carelessness of the justices in imposing this rate, or the negligence of the constables in collecting it, or the backwardness of the inhabitants in paying the same, or all these together overslipped the time and withheld the satisfaction. Hereon down comes a messenger with sharp letters from the Officers of the Green Cloth. The conclusion ensued, that his charges must be borne, and a higher price disbursed for the supply. Thus it fareth to and fro, and the Cornish men seem to hold a wolf by the ears: for to make payment the people are unwilling, as in a charge heretofore unusual, to undergo the managing hereof, the justices strain courtesy, as in a matter nothing plausible, and appertaining to over-many partners for the well effecting, and yet to break they are both afraid, suspecting that a heavier load will follow, if this composition be once set at large.

These commodities go not unaccompanied with their inconveniences, for to Cornwall also hath Pandora's box been opened. One is, that the far distance from the higher seats of justice rippeth a wider gap to intruding injuries, and increaseth the charge and time of procuring their redress. Which due occasion of discouragement the worst conditioned and least cliented pettifoggers do yet (under the sweet bait of revenge) convert to a more plentiful prosecution of actions. The ordinary trade of these men is, where they perceive a spark of displeasure kindling, to increase the flame with their bellows of persuasion. 'Hath such a one abused you?' saith he. 'Anger him a little, that breaking out into some outrageous words you may take advantage thereof, and you shall see how we will hamper him; I warrant you he shall fetch an errand to London, and bear part of your charges too.' After the game hath been brought in by this windlass, the poor soul is bound not to release his adversary without his attorney's consent, who plieth the matter with so good a stomach as he eateth the kernel whilst they fight about the shell. At last, when the fountain of his client's purse is drawn dry by his extravagant fees of *pro consilio* [consultation], *pro expeditione* [forwarding the matter], *pro amicitia Vicecomitis* [getting the sheriff on our side], &c, besides the packing between the under-sheriff and him, of docketing out writs never sued forth, the mediation of friends must shut up the matter in a compromise. Another discommodity groweth, that whereas London furnisheth all provisions (even tin, and such others arising in the same country) of best stuff, fashion, store, and cheapness, the hard procuring and far carriage addeth an extraordinary increase of price to the Cornish buyers; and for matters of benefit or preferment by suits at Court, either the opportunity is passed before notice can arrive so far, or the following there and loss the whiles at home will require a great and assured gain in the principal, to warrant the hope of a saving bargain in the appurtenance.

Touching the temperature of Cornwall, the air thereof is cleansed as with bellows by the billows, and flowing and ebbing of the sea, and therethrough becometh pure and subtle, and by consequence healthful, so as the inhabitants do seldom take a ruthful and reaving experience of those harms which infectious diseases use to carry with them. But yet I have noted that this so piercing an air is apter to preserve than recover health, especially in any languishing sickness which hath possessed strangers; neither know I whether I may impute to this goodness of the air that upon the return of our fleet from the Portugal action, 1589, the diseases which the soldiers brought home with them did grow more grievous as they carried the same farther into the land, than it fell out at Plymmouth, where they landed; for there the same was, though infectious, yet not so contagious, and though pestilential, yet not the very pestilence, as afterwards it proved in other places.

The Spring visiteth not these quarters so timely as the eastern parts. Summer imparteth a very temperate heat, recompensing his slow fostering of the fruits with their kindly ripening. Autumn bringeth a somewhat late harvest, specially to the middle of the shire, where they seldom in their corn before Michaelmas. Winter, by reason of the south's near neighbourhood and sea's warm breath, favoureth it with a milder cold than elsewhere, so as upon both coasts the frost and snow come very seldom, and make a speedy departure. This notwithstanding, the country is much subject to storms, which fetching a large course in the open sea, do from thence violently assault the dwellers at land, and leave them uncovered houses, pared hedges, and dwarf-grown trees as witnesses of their force and fury; yea, even the hard stones and iron bars of the windows do fret to be so continually grated. One kind of these storms they call a flaw, or flaugh, which is a mighty gale of wind passing suddenly to the shore, and working strong effects upon whatsoever it encountereth in his way.

The Cornish soil, for the most part, is lifted up into many hills, some great, some little of quantity, some steep, some easy for ascent, and parted in sunder by short and narrow valleys. A shallow earth doth cover their outside, the substance of the rest consisteth ordinarily in rocks and shelf, which maketh them hard for manurance, and subject to a dry Summer's parching. The middle part of the shire (saving the enclosures about some few towns and villages) lieth waste and open, showeth a blackish colour, beareth heath and spiry grass, and serveth in a manner only to summer cattle. That which bordereth upon either side of the sea, through the inhabitants' good husbandry of enclosing, sanding, and other dressing, carrieth a better hue and more profitable quality. Meadow ground it affordeth little, pasture for cattle and sheep, store enough, corn ground plenty. Hills of greatest name and height are, Hinxton, Rowtor, Brown Welly, St Agnes, Haynborough, the four boroughs, Roche, Carn Bray, and the two Castellan Danis.

In the rest of this earthy description I will begin with such minerals as her bowels yield forth, and then pass on to those things of growing and feeling life which upon her face do relieve themselves.

These minerals are not so deep buried by nature in the entrails of the earth, nor so closely couched among the rocks, but that desire of gain with the instrument of art can dig them up. They may be divided into stones and metals.

Quarry stones are of sundry sorts, and serve to divers purposes. For walling there are rough and slate; the rough maketh speedier building, the slate surer. For windows, dornes [door frames], and chimneys, moor stone carrieth chiefest reckoning. That name is bestowed on it by the moors or waste ground, where the same is found in great quantity, either lying upon the ground or very little under. This stone answereth the charge of fetching with the fairness of its whitish colour containing certain glimmering sparkles, and countervaileth its great hardness in working with the profit of long endurance, nature having ordained the same, as of purpose, to withstand the fretting weather. There are also three other sorts of stones serving to the same use, and hewed with less though differing labour: Pentuan digged out of the sea cliffs, and in colour somewhat resembling grey marble; Caraclouse black, not unlike the jet; the third taken out of inland quarries, and not much differing from the eastern freestone.

The sea strand also in many places affordeth pebble stones, which, washed out of the earth or falling from the rocks and there lying loose, are by often rolling of the waves wrought to a kind of roundness, and serve very handsomely for paving of streets and courts.

For covering of houses there are three sorts of slate, which from that use take the name of heling-stones [hele = cover over]: the first and best blue, the second sage-leaf coloured, the third and meanest, grey. The blue, and so the rest, are commonly found under the walling slate, when the depth hath brought the workmen to the water. This slate is in substance thin, in colour fair, in weight light, in lasting strong, and generally carrieth so good regard, as (besides the supply for home provision) great store is yearly conveyed by shipping both to other parts of the realm, and also beyond the seas, into Brittany and Netherland.

They make lime, moreover, of another kind of marl-stone, either by burning a great quantity thereof together, with a fervent fire of furze, or by maintaining a continual though lesser heat with stone coal in smaller kilns; this is accounted the better cheap, but that yieldeth the whiter lime.

Touching metals: copper is found in sundry places, but with what gain to the searchers I have not been curious to enquire, nor they hasty to reveal, for at one mine (of which I took view) the ore was shipped to be refined in Wales, either to save cost in fuel, or to conceal the profit.

Neither hath nature denied silver to Cornwall, though Cicero excluded the same out of all Britain, and if we may believe our chroniclers' reports, who ground themselves upon authentic records, King Edward I and King Edward III reaped some good benefit thereof. But for our present experience, what she proffereth with the one hand she seemeth to pull back with the other, whereof some gentlemen not long since made trial to their loss; howbeit, neither are they discouraged by this success, nor others from the like attempt.

Tinners do also find little hopps of gold amongst their ore, which they keep in quills, and sell to the goldsmiths oftentimes with little better gain than Glaucus' exchange. Yea, it is not altogether barren of precious stones and pearl; for diamonds are in many places found cleaving to those rocks out of which the tin is digged. They are polished, squared, and pointed by nature, their quantity from a pea to a walnut; in blackness and hardness they come behind the right ones, and yet I have known some of them set on so good a foil as at first sight they might appose [test] a not unskilful lapidary. The pearl (though here not aptly ranged) breed in big oysters and mussels, greater in quantity than acceptable for goodness, as neither round nor Orient. Perhaps Caesar spoiled the best beds when he made that gay coat of them to present his grand-dame Venus.

Cornwall is also not altogether destitute of agates and white coral, as by credible relation I have learned.

But why seek we in corners for petty commodities, whenas the only mineral of Cornish tin openeth so large a field to the country's benefit? This is in working so pliant, for sight so fair, and in use so necessary, as thereby the inhabitants gain wealth, the merchants traffic, and the whole realm a reputation; and with such plenty thereof hath God stuffed the bowels of this little angle, that (as Astiages dreamed of his daughter) it overfloweth England, watereth Christendom, and is derived to a great part of the world besides. In travelling abroad, in tarrying at home, in eating and drinking, in doing aught of pleasure or necessity, tin, either in its own shape, or transformed into other fashions, is always requisite, always ready for our service. But I shall rather disgrace than endear it by mine over-weak commendation, and sooner tire myself than draw the fountain of his praises dry. Let this therefore suffice, that it cannot be of mean price which hath found with it diamonds, amongst it gold, and in it silver.

The Cornish tinners hold a strong imagination that in the withdrawing of Noah's flood to the sea, the same took his course from east to west, violently breaking up and forcibly carrying with it the earth, trees, and rocks which lay any thing loosely near the upper face of the ground. To confirm the likelihood of which supposed truth, they do many times dig up whole and huge timber trees, which they conceive at that deluge to have been overturned and whelmed; but whether then or since, probable it is that some such cause produced this effect. Hence it cometh, that albeit the tin lay couched at first in certain streaks amongst the rocks, like a tree or the veins in a man's body, from the depth whereof the main lode spreadeth out his branches until they approach the open air, yet they have now two kinds of tin works, stream and lode; for (say they) the forementioned flood carried, together with the moved rocks and earth, so much of the lode as was enclosed therein, and at the assuaging left the same scattered here and there in the valleys and rivers where it passed, which being sought and digged is called stream work. Under this title they comprise also the moor works growing from the like occasion. They maintain these works to have been very ancient and first wrought by Jews with pickaxes of holm, box, and hartshorn; they prove this by the name of those places yet enduring; to wit, Attall Sarazin, in English, the Jews'

Offcast, and by those tools daily found amongst the rubble of such works. And it may well be, that as acorns made good bread before Ceres taught the use of corn, and sharp stones served the Indians for knives until the Spaniards brought them iron, so in the infancy of knowledge these poor instruments, for want of better, did supply a turn. There are also taken up in such works certain little tools' heads of brass which some term thunder-axes, but they make small show of any profitable use. Neither were the Romans ignorant of this trade, as may appear by a brass coin of Domitian's, found in one of these works and fallen into my hands; and perhaps under one of those Flavians the Jewish workmen made here their first arrival.

They discover these works by certain tin-stones lying on the face of the ground, which they term shoad, as shed from the main lode, and made somewhat smooth and round by the water's washing and wearing. Where the finding of these affordeth a tempting likelihood, the tinners go to work, casting up trenches before them, in depth five or six foot, more or less, as the loose ground went, and three or four in breadth, gathering up such shoad as this turning of the earth doth offer to their sight. If any river thwart them, and that they resolve to search his bed, he is trained by a new channel from his former course. This yieldeth a speedy and gainful recompense to the adventurers of the search, but I hold it little beneficial to the owners of the soil, for those low grounds, beforetime fruitful, having herethrough their wrong side turned outwards, accuse the tinners' injury by their succeeding barrenness.

To find the lode works, their first labour is also employed in seeking this shoad, which either lieth open on the grass, or but shallowly covered. Having found any such, they conjecture by the sight of the ground which way the flood came that brought it thither, and so give a guess at the place whence it was broken off. There they sink a shaft, or pit, of five or six foot in length, two or three foot in breadth, and seven or eight foot in depth, to prove whether they may so meet with the lode. By this shaft they also discern which was the quick ground (as they call it) which moved with the flood, and which the firm, wherein no such shoad doth lie. If they miss the lode in one place, they sink a like shaft in another beyond that, commonly farther up towards the hill, and so a third and a fourth, until they light at last upon it. But you may not conceive that every likelihood doth ever prove a certainty, for divers have been hindered through bestowing charges in seeking and not finding, and many undone in finding and not speeding, whilst a fair show tempting them to much cost hath in the end failed in substance and made the adventurers bankrupt of their hope and purse.

Some have found tin works of great value through means no less strange than extraordinary, to wit, by dreams; as in Edward VI's time, a gentlewoman, heir to one Tresculierd and wife to Lanyne, dreamed that a man of seemly personage told her how in such a tenement of her land she should find so great store of tin as would serve to enrich both herself and her posterity. This she revealed to her husband, and he, putting the same in trial, found a work which in four years was worth him well near so many thousand pounds. Moreover, one Taprel, lately living, and dwelling in the parish of the hundred of West called St Niot, by a like dream of his daughter (see the luck of women) made the like essay, met with the effect, farmed the work of the unwitting lord of the soil, and grew thereby to good state of wealth. The same report passeth as current touching sundry others, but I will not bind any man's credit though that of the authors have herein swayed mine; and yet he that will afford his ear to astrologers and natural philosophers shall have it filled with many discourses of the constellation of the heavens and the constitution of men's bodies, fitting to this purpose.

There are, that leaving these trades of new searching, do take in hand such old stream and lode works as by the former adventurers have been given over, and oftentimes they find good store of tin, both in the rubble cast up before, as also in veins which the first workmen followed not. From hence there groweth a diversity in opinion amongst such gentlemen as by judgement and experience can look into these matters, some of them supposing that the tin groweth, and others that it only separateth from the consumed offal. But whosoever readeth that which Francis Leandro hath written touching the iron minerals in the isle of Elba will cleave perhaps to a third conceit, for he avoucheth that the trenches out of which the ore there is digged, within twenty or thirty years become alike full again of the same metal as at first, and he confirmeth it by suitable examples borrowed from Clearchus, of marble in Paros Island, and of salt in India, deducing thence this reason, that the air and water replenishing the void room, through the power of the universal agent and some peculiar celestial influence, are turned into the self substance, and so by consequence neither the ore groweth nor the earth consumeth away. And this opinion Münster in his *Cosmography* doth seem to underprop, affirming that near the city of Apolonia in Dalmatia the veins whence brass is digged are filled in like manner. So doth he report that near Ptolomais there lieth a round valley, out of which glassy sand being taken, the winds fill the pit again from the upper part of the adjoining mountains, which matter is converted into the former substance, and that even metals thrown into this place do undergo the like metamorphosis.

The colour both of the shoad and lode resembleth his bed, as the sea sand doth the cliffs, and is so diversified to reddish, blackish, dusky, and such other earthy colours.

If the lode wherein the tin lieth carrieth a foot and a half in breadth, and be not over barren, it is accounted a very rich work, but commonly the same exceedeth not a foot, unless many lodes run together.

When the new found work enticeth with probability of profit, the discoverer doth commonly associate himself with some more partners, because the charge amounteth mostly very high for any one man's purse, except lined beyond ordinary, to reach unto; and if the work do fail, many shoulders will more easily support the burden. These partners consist either of such tinners as work to their own behoof, or of such adventurers as put in hired labourers. The hirelings stand at a certain wages, either by the day, which may be about eightpence, or for the year, being between four and six pound, as their deserving can drive the bargain, at both which rates they must find [support] themselves.

If the work carry some importance, and require the travail of many hands, that hath his name, and they their overseer whom they term their captain: such are the *Pel*, *Whilancleuth*, in English, The Work of the Ditches: *Pulstean*, that is, The Miry Head: *Crueg braaz*, The great Borough: Saint Marget's, and many surnamed Balls, which betoken the vales where the works are set on foot.

The captain's office bindeth him to sort each workman his task, to see them apply their labour, to make timely provision for binding the work with frames of timber if need exact it, to place pumps for drawing off water, and to give such other directions. In most places their toil is so extreme as they cannot endure it above four hours in a day, but are succeeded by spells; the residue of the time they wear out at quoits, kayles [skittles], or like idle exercises. Their calendar also alloweth them more holidays than are warranted by the Church, our laws, or their own profit.

Their ordinary tools are a pickaxe of iron about sixteen inches long, sharpened at the one end to peck, and flat-headed at the other to drive certain little iron wedges wherewith they cleave the rocks. They have also a broad shovel, the utter part of iron, the middle of timber, into which the staff is slopewise fastened.

Their manner of working in the lode mines is to follow the lode as it lieth, either sidelong or downright; both ways the deeper they sink the greater they find the lode. When they light upon a small vein, or chance to lose the lode which they wrought, by means of certain strings that may hap to cross it, they begin at another place near hand and so draw by guess to the main lode again. If the lode lie right down they follow it sometimes to the depth of forty or fifty fathom. These lode works, Diodorus Siculus (Book V Chapter 8) seemeth to point at where he saith that the inhabitants of Velerium Promontory [Land's End] dig up tin out of rocky ground. From some of their bottoms you shall at noonday descry the stars. The workmen are let down and taken up in a stirrup by two men who wind the rope.

If the lode lie slopewise, the tinners dig a convenient depth and then pass forward underground so far as the air will yield them breathing, which, as it beginneth to fail, they sink a shaft down thither from the top to admit a renewing vent, which notwithstanding, their work is most by candle-light. In these passages they meet sometimes with very loose earth, sometimes with exceeding hard rocks, and sometimes with great streams of water.

The loose earth is propped by frames of timber-work as they go, and yet now and then falling down, either presseth the poor workmen to death or stoppeth them from returning. To part the rocks they have the forementioned axes and wedges, with which, mostly, they make speedy way, and yet (not seldom) are so tied by the teeth as a good workman shall hardly be able to hew three feet in the space of so many weeks. While they thus play the moldwarps, unsavoury damps [gases] do here and there distemper their heads, though not with so much danger in the consequence as annoyance for the present.

For conveying away the water they pray in aid of sundry devices, as adits, pumps, and wheels driven by a stream and interchangeably filling and emptying two buckets, with many such like, all which notwithstanding, the springs so encroach upon these inventions as in sundry places they are driven to keep men, and somewhere horses also, at work both day and night without ceasing, and in some all this will not serve the turn. For supplying such hard services they have always fresh men at hand.

They call it the bringing of an adit, or audit, when they begin to trench without, and carry the same through the ground to the tin work somewhat deeper than the water doth lie, thereby to give it passage away.

This adit they either fetch athwart the whole lode, or right from the branch where they work, as the next valley ministereth fittest opportunity for soonest cutting into the hill, and therefore a gentleman of good knowledge deduceth this name of adit, *Ab aditu ad aquas* ['from the approach to the springs']. Surely the practice is cunning in device, costly in charge, and long in effecting, and yet when all is done many times the lode falleth away and they may sing with Augustus' bird, *Opera et impensa periit* [work and effort are wasted]. If you did see how aptly they cast the ground for conveying the water, by compassings and turnings to shun such hills and valleys as let [hinder] them by their too much height or lowness, you would wonder how so great skill could couch in so base a cabin as their (otherwise) thickclouded brains.

As much almost doth it exceed credit that the tin, for and in so small quantity, digged up with so great toil, and passing afterwards through the managing of so many hands ere it come to sale, should be any way able to acquit the cost; for being once brought above ground in the stone, it is first broken in pieces with hammers, and then carried either in wains or on horses' backs to a stamping-mill, where three, and in some places six great logs of timber, bound at the ends with iron, and lifted up and down by a wheel driven with the water, do break it smaller. If the stones be over moist they are dried by the fire in an iron cradle or grate.

From the stamping-mill it passeth to the crazing-mill, which between two grinding stones, turned also with a water wheel, bruiseth the same to a fine sand. Howbeit, of late times they mostly use wet stampers, and so have no need of the crazing-mills for their best stuff, but only for the crust of their tails.

The stream, after it hath forsaken the mill, is made to fall by certain degrees, one somewhat distant from another, upon each of which at every descent lieth a green turf, three or four foot square and one foot thick. On this the tinner layeth a certain portion of the sandy tin, and with his shovel softly tosseth the same to and fro, that through this stirring the water which runneth over it may wash away the light earth from the tin, which of a heavier substance lieth fast on the turf. Having so cleansed one portion, he setteth the same aside and beginneth with another, until his labour take end with his task. The best of those turfs (for all sorts serve not) are fetched about two miles to the eastward of St Michael's Mount, where at a low water they cast aside the sand and dig them up; they are full of roots of trees, and on some of them nuts have been found, which confirmeth my former assertion of the sea's intrusion. After it is thus washed, they put the remnant into a wooden dish, broad, flat, and round being about two foot over and having two handles fastened at the sides, by which they softly shog the same to and fro in the water between their legs as they sit over it, until whatsoever of the earthy substance that was yet left be flitted away. Some of later time, with a slighter invention and lighter labour, do cause certain boys to stir it up and down with their feet, which worketh the same effect. The residue, after this often cleansing, they call black tin, which is proportionably divided to every of the adventurers when the lord's part hath been first deducted upon the whole.

Then doth each man carry his portion to the blowing-house, where the same is melted with charcoal fire, blown by a great pair of bellows moved with a water-wheel, and so cast into pieces of a long and thick squareness, from three hundred to four hundred pound weight, at which time the owner's mark is set thereupon. The last remove is to the place of coinage, which I shall touch hereafter. I have already told you how great charge the tinner undergoeth before he can bring his ore to this last mill, whereto if you add his care and cost in buying the wood for this service, in felling, framing, and piling it to be burned, in fetching the same when it is coaled, through such far, foul, and cumbersome ways to the blowing-house, together with the blowers' two or three months' extreme and increasing labour, sweltering heat, danger of scalding their bodies, burning the houses, casting away the work, and lastly their ugly countenances tanned with smoke and besmeared with sweat: all these things (I say) being duly considered, I know not whether you would more marvel either whence a sufficient gain should arise to countervail so manifold expenses, or that any gain could train men to undertake such pains and peril. But there let us leave them, since their own will doth bring them thither. During the tin's thus melting in the blowing-house, divers light sparkles thereof are by the forcible wind which the bellows sendeth forth, driven up to the thatched roof: for which cause the owners do, once in seven or eight years, burn those houses, and find so much of this light tin in the ashes as payeth for the new building, with a gainful overplus. A strange practice (certes) for thrift's sake to set our house on fire. Others do frame the tunnels of the chimneys very large and slope, therein to harbour these sparkles and so save the burning. This casualty may be worth the owner some ten pound by the year, or better, if his mill have store of suitors. But sithence I gathered sticks for the building of this poor nest, Sir Francis Godolphin (whose kind help hath much advanced this my playing labour) entertained a Dutch mineral man, and taking light from his experience but building thereon far more profitable conclusions of his own invention, hath practised a more saving way in these matters, and besides made tin with good profit of that refuse which the tinners rejected as nothing worth.

We will now proceed to take a view of the orders and customs most generally used among the tinners.

Their works, both stream and lode, lie either in several or in wastrel, that is, in enclosed grounds or in commons. In several, no man can search for tin without leave first obtained from the lord of the soil, who, when any mine is found, may work it wholly himself, or associate partners, or set it out at a farm certain, or leave it unwrought at his pleasure. In wastrel it is lawful for any man to make trial of his fortune that way, provided that he acknowledge the lord's right by sharing out to him a certain part, which they call toll: a custom savouring more of indifferency [fairness] than the tinners' constitutions in Devon, which enable them to dig for tin in any man's ground, enclosed or unenclosed, without licence, tribute, or satisfaction: wherethrough it appeareth that the law-makers rather respected their own benefit than equity, the true touch of all laws. The wastrel works are reckoned among chattels, and may pass by word or will. When a mine is found in any such place, the first discoverer aimeth how far it is likely to extend, and then at the four corners of his limited proportion diggeth up three turfs, and the like (if he list) on the sides, which they term bounding, and within that compass every other man is restrained from searching. These bounds he is bound to renew once every year, and also in most places to bestow some time in working the mine, otherwise he loseth this privilege. The work thus found and bounded, look how many men do labour therein, so many doles or shares they make thereof, and proportionably divide the gain and charges. The lord of the soil is most-where allowed liberty to place one workman in every fifteen for himself, at like hand with the adventurers, if he be so disposed.

They measure their black tin by the gill, the topliff, the dish, and the foot, which containeth a pint, a pottle, a gallon, and towards two gallons.

Towns specially privileged for the coinages are Helston, Truro, Lostwithiel, and Liskerd. The times of coinage come twice in the year; viz. about Midsummer and Michaelmas: but because it falleth out very often that the tin which is wrought cannot be blown and brought thither against the limited days, there are, in favour of the tinners, certain later times assigned, which they term Post-coinages.

The officers deputed to manage this coinage are, porters to bear the tin, peizers to weigh it, a Steward, Comptroller, and Receiver to keep the account: every of which have entertainment from her Majesty, and receive a fee out of the coined tin.

For the manner of coinage, the blocks or pieces of tin are brought into a great room ordained for that purpose, and there first peized, then tasted, that is, proved whether they be soft tin or hard, and after marked with her Majesty's stamp. To the hard (less worth by fifty shillings in the thousand than the soft) the letter H is added ere it comes from the blowing-house. Each thousand must answer forty shillings to the Queen, which, with the other incident fees being satisfied, then and not before, it is lawful for the owner to alienate and distract the same.

But about the price there groweth much ado between the merchants and the owners before they can jump to an agreement. The merchant unfoldeth his pack of strange news, which either he brought with him from London (where most of them dwell) or forged by the way, telling what great likelihood there is of wars, what dangers of pirates at sea, how much of the forebought tin lieth on their hands, &c. The owner, on the other side, stoppeth his ears against these charms, answers his news with the Spaniards' *Credo en Dios* [I trust to God], encounters his reasons with the present scarcity and charge of getting and working tin, and so keeping up the price, *Iniquum petit, ut aequum ferat.* [He asks an unfair price to get a fair one.] In the end, after much bidding and lowing, varying and delaying, commonly that merchant who hath most money to bestow, and that owner who hath most tin to sell, do make the price, at which rate the merchant is bound to yield present payment for so much tin as shall be brought him, and of necessity must bargain for ten thousand at the least. Others, notwithstanding, are not bound to buy or sell at this price, but every man left at liberty to make his best market.

The tin so sold hath usually amounted heretofore to the worth of thirty or forty thousand pounds in money, and carried price between twenty and thirty pounds the thousand, sometimes higher and sometimes lower, according to the quick vent [sale] and abundance, or the dead sale and scarcity; wherein yet some have observed that this so profitable and vendible merchandise riseth not to a proportionable enhancement with other less beneficial and affected commodities, and they impute it partly to the eastern buyers' packing, partly to the owners not venting and venturing the same.

Here I must either crave, or take, leave of the Londoners to lay open the hard dealing of their tin merchants in this trade. When any western gentleman or person of account wanteth money to defray his expenses at London, he resorteth to one of the tin merchants of his acquaintance to borrow some; but they shall as soon wrest the club out of Hercules' fist as one penny out of their fingers, unless they give bond for every twenty pounds so taken in loan to deliver a thousand pounds weight of tin at the next coinage, which shall be within two or three months, or at farthest within half a year after, at which time the price of every thousand will not fail to be at least twenty-three, perhaps twenty-five pounds: yea, and after promise made, the party must be driven (with some indignity) to make three or four errands to his house ere he shall get the money delivered. In this sort, some one merchant will have five hundred pounds out beforehand, reaping thereby a double commodity, both of excessive gain for his loan, and of assurance to be served with tin for his money. This, they say, is no usury, forsooth, because the price of tin is not certainly known beforehand (for once only within these twelve years, of set purpose to escape the penalty of the law, they brought it a little under twenty pounds the thousand) but if to take above fifty in the hundred be extremity, whatsoever name you list to give it, this in truth can be none other than cutthroat and abominable dealing. I will not condemn all such as use this trade, neither yet acquit those who make greatest pretense of zeal in religion; and it may be that some upon by-respects find somewhat friendly usage in usance at some of their hands, but the common voice saith, that 'for the most part they are naught all'.

And yet how bad soever this fashion may justly be accounted, certain of the same countrymen do pass far beyond it, as thus: the merchant, that he may stand assured to have tin for his money at the time of coinage or deliverance, besides his trade of loan above mentioned, layeth out divers sums beforehand unto certain Cornishmen, owners of tin works or otherwise of known sufficiency, who are bound to deliver for the same so many thousands of tin as the money shall amount unto after the price agreed upon at the coinages. To these hungry flies the poor labouring tinner resorteth, desiring some money before the time of his pay at the deliverance; the other puts him off at first, answering he hath none to spare; in the end, when the poor man is driven through necessity to renew his suit, he falls to questioning what he will do with the money. Saith the tinner, 'I will buy bread and meat for myself and my household, and shoes, hosen, petticoats, and such like stuff for my wife and children.' Suddenly herein this owner becomes a petty chapman; 'I will serve thee,' saith he; he delivers him so much ware as shall amount to forty shillings, in which he cuts him half in half for the price, and four nobles in money, for which the poor wretch is bound in Darby's bonds [a notorious money-lender's contract: later to become slang for handcuffs] to deliver him two hundred weight of tin at the next coinage, which may then be worth five pounds, or four at the very least. And as mischief still creeps onwards, this extreme dealing of the London merchant and country chapman in white tin is imitated (or rather exceeded) by the wealthier sort of tinners themselves in the black, by laying out their money after thus much the mark: which trade, though subtle and dark, I will open as plainly as I can.

A foot of black tin (as is before said) containeth in measure two gallons; the weight uncertainly followeth the goodness. A foot of good moor-tin (which is counted the best sort) will weigh about four score pound; of the mine tin (which is meaner) fifty-two pound; of the worst fifty pound. Two pound of good black tin, being melted, will yield one of white: twenty-eight or thirty foot of the best, forty; of the middle, fifty-two, of the meanest, a thousand.

Now the wealthiest sort of tinners, laying out part of their money beforehand, buy this black tin of the poor labourers, after so much the mark: that is, look how many marks there are in the price, made at the coinage for the thousand, so many two pence halfpenny, three pence, or four pence, partly after the goodness, and partly according to the hard conscience of the one, and the necessity of the other, shall he have for the foot: as if the price be twenty-six pound, thirteen shillings and fourpence the thousand, therein are forty marks; then shall the poor tinner receive of him who dealeth most friendly, for every foot of his black tin (of which as was said about thirty will make a thousand) forty times four pence, which amounteth to twenty pounds the thousand; whereas that foot at the price is worth above five pence the mark. Likewise will he pay for the meaner black tin (of which about forty foot will make a thousand) three pence the mark, which is ten shillings the foot, and so shall he have also after twenty pound for the thousand: for the worse they give less, rateably. By which proportion, how uncertain soever the goodness of the tin, or the greatness of the price do fall, their gain of a fourth part at least riseth always uncertainly. Whereto adding, that they lay out beforehand but a proportion of the money due, and that only for some final time, you shall find it grow to the highest degree of extremity.

But whether it proceedeth from this hard dealing, or for that the tinner's whole family give themselves to a lazy kind of life and depend only upon his labour and gains, which often ill-succeeding adventures and such over-dear bought tin daily impair, or from both these together, once it hath been duly observed that the parishes where tin is wrought rest in a meaner plight of wealth than those which want this damageable commodity, and that as by abandoning this trade they amend, so by reviving the same they decay again, whereas husbandry yieldeth that certain gain in a mediocrity which tin works rather promise than perform in a larger measure.

Let us now examine what course of justice is held for deciding such controversies as befall in tin causes and with what privileges they are endowed and encouraged.

After such time as the Jews by their extreme dealings had worn themselves first out of the love of the English inhabitants, and afterwards out of the land itself, and so left the mines unwrought, it happened that certain gentlemen, being lords of seven tithings in Blackmoore, whose grounds were best stored with this mineral, grew desirous to renew this benefit; and so upon suit made to Edmond Earl of Cornwall, son to Richard King of the Romans, they obtained from him a charter with sundry privileges, amongst which it was granted them to keep a court and hold plea of all actions, life, limb, and land excepted, in consideration whereof the said lords accorded to pay the Earl a halfpenny for every pound of tin which should be wrought, and that, for better answering this tax, the said tin should be brought to certain places purposely appointed, and there peized, coined, and kept until the Earl's dues were satisfied. Again, the lords of these tithings were, for their parts, authorised to manage all stannary causes, and for that intent to hold parliaments at their discretion; and in regard of their labour there was allotted unto them the toll tin within those tithings, which their successors do yet enjoy. This charter was to be kept in one of the church steeples within those tithings, and the seal had a pickaxe and shovel in saltire graven therein. This I received by report of the late Master William Carnsew, a gentleman of good quality, discretion, and learning, and well experienced in these mineral causes, who avouched himself an eye-witness of that charter, though now it be not extant.

Howbeit, I have learned, that in former time the tinners obtained a charter from King John, and afterwards another from King Edward I, which were again expounded, confirmed and enlarged by Parliament in the fiftieth year of Edward III, and lastly strengthened by King Henry VII.

King Edward I's charter granteth them liberty of selling their tin, to their best behoof. *Nisi* (saith he) *nos ipsi emere voluerimus* [unless we should wish to buy it ourselves]. Upon which ground certain persons in the reigns of King Edward and Queen Marie sought to make use of this preemption (as I have been informed) but either crossed in the prosecution or defeated in their expectation, gave it over again which vain success could not yet discourage some others of later times from the like attempt, alleging many reasons how it might prove beneficial both to her Highness and the country, and prejudicial to none save only the merchants, who practised a far worse kind of preemption, as hath been before expressed. This for a while was hotly onsetted and a reasonable price offered, but (upon what ground I know not) soon cooled again. Yet afterwards it received a second life, and at Michaelmas term 1599 the Cornishmen, then in London, were called before some of the principal Lords of her Majesty's Council, and the matter there debated, by the Lord Warden, in behalf of the country, and certain others deputed for the merchants, who had set this suit on foot. In the end it grew to a conclusion, and Articles were drawn and signed, but they also proved of void effect.

Last of all, the said Lord Warden, in the beginning of November 1600, called an assembly of tinners at Lostwithiel, the place accustomed, empanelled a jury of twenty-four tinners, signified her Majesty's pleasure both for a new imposition of six pound on every thousand that should be transported (over and above the former forty shillings, and sixteen shillings already payable) as also that her Highness would disburse four thousand pound in loan to the tinners, for a year's space, and be repaid in tin at a certain rate.

By the forementioned ancient charters there is assigned a Warden of the Stannaries, who supplieth the place both of a judge for law and of a chancellor for conscience, and so taketh hearing of causes, either *in forma juris* or *de jure et aequo* [strictly in law or by law and equity]. He substituteth some gentleman in the shire of good calling and discretion to be his Vice-Warden, from whom either party, complainant or defendant, may appeal to him, as from him (a case of rare experience) to the Lords of the Council, and from their Honours to her Majesty's person. Other appeal, or removing to the common-law, they gainsay.

The gaol for stannary causes is kept at Lostwithiel, and that office is annexed to the Comptrollership. The tinners of the whole shire are divided into four quarters, two called Moores, of the places where the tin is wrought, viz. Foymoore and Blackemoore, the other Tiwarnaill and Penwith. To each of these is assigned by the Lord Warden a Steward, who keepeth his court once in every three weeks. They are termed Stannary Courts, of the Latin word *stannum*, in English tin, and hold plea of whatsoever action of debt or trespass, whereto anyone dealing with black or white tin, either as plaintiff or defendant, is a party. Their manner of trial consisteth in the verdict given by a jury of six tinners, according to which the Steward pronounceth judgement. He that will spare credit to the common report shall conceive an ill opinion touching the slippings of both witnesses and jurors sometimes in these courts; for it is said that the witnesses have not sticked now and then to fasten their evidence, rather for serving a turn than for manifesting a truth, and that the jurors' verdict hath savoured more of affection than of reason, especially in controversies grown between strangers and some of the same parts. And such fault-finders vouch divers causes of this partiality. One, that when they are sworn, they use to add this word, 'my conscience', as the Romans did their *Ex animi mei sententia* [in the opinion of my soul] which is suspected to imply a conceited enlargement of their oath. Another, that the variety of customs, which in every place (well-near) differ one from another, yieldeth them in a manner an unlimited scope to aver what they list, and so to close the best lawyer's mouth with this one speech, 'Our custom is contrary'. And lastly, that they presume upon a kind of impunity, because these six men juries fall not within compass of the Star chamber's censure, and yet the Lord Wardens have now and then made the pillory punishment of some, a spectacle, example and warning to the residue.

For mine own part, I can in these tin cases plead but a hearsay experience, and therefore will only infer that as there is no smoke without a fire, so commonly the smoke is far greater than the fire. Strange it were, and not to be excepted [misprint for expected?], that all poor tin jurors and witnesses should in such a remote corner always conform themselves to the precise rule of uprightness, when we see in the open light of our public assizes so many more judicious and substantial persons now and then to swerve from the same.

In matters of important consequence appertaining to the whole stannary the Lord Warden, or his Under-Warden, useth to empanel a jury of four and twenty principal tinners, which consist of six out of every quarter, returnable by the mayors of the four stannary towns, and whose acts do bind the residue.

Next to the lifeless things follow those which partake a growing life, and then a feeling.

The women and children in the west part of Cornwall do use to make mats of a small and fine kind of bents [wiry grasses] there growing, which for their warm and well wearing are carried by sea to London and other parts of the realm and serve to cover floors and walls. These bents grow in sandy fields, and are knit from over the head in narrow breadths after a strange fashion.

Of herbs and roots for the pot and medicine, Cornishmen enjoy a like portion in proportion with other shires, which somewhere also receiveth an increase by the sowing and planting of such as are brought thither from beyond the seas. The like may be said of roots and salads for the table, save that (I suppose) Cornwall naturally bringeth forth greater store of seaholm and samphire than is found in any other county of this realm. The seaholm root preserved either in syrup or by candying is accepted for a great restorative. Some of the galty [boggy] grounds do also yield plenty of *rosa solis* [sundew]. Moreover nature's liberal hand decketh many of the sea cliffs with wild hyssop, sage, pellamountain [thyme], marjoram, rosemary, and suchlike well-savouring herbs.

In times past the Cornish people gave themselves principally (and in a manner wholly) to the seeking of tin, and neglected husbandry, so as the neighbours of Devon and Somerset shires hired their pastures at a rent and stored them with their own cattle.

As for tillage, it came far short of feeding the inhabitants' mouths, who were likewise supplied weekly at their markets from those places with many hundred quarters of corn and horse-loads of bread. But when the tin works began to fail and the people to increase, this double necessity drove them to play the good husbands and to provide corn of their own. Labour brought plenty, plenty cheapness, and cheapness sought a vent beyond the seas, some by procuring licence, and more by stealth (if at least the common bruit do not wrong them with a slander) so as, had not the embargo with Spain (whither most were transported) foreclosed this trade Cornwall was likely in a few years to reap no little wealth by the same. And yet, whosoever looketh into the endeavour which the Cornish husbandman is driven to use about his tillage shall find the travail painful, the time tedious, and the expenses very chargeable. For first, about May, they cut up all the grass of that ground, which must be newly broken, into turfs, which they call beating. These turfs they raise up somewhat in the midst, that the wind and sun may the sooner dry them. The inside turned outwards drieth more speedily, but the outside can better brook the change of weather. After they have been thoroughly dried, the husbandman pileth them in little heaps, and so burneth them to ashes.

Then do they bring in sea sand of greater or lesser quantity, partly after their nearness to the places from which it is fetched, and partly by the good husbandry and ability of the tiller. An ordinary horse will carry two sacks of sand, and of such the borderers on the sea do bestow sixty at least in every acre, but most husbands double that number. The inland soil requireth not so large a proportion, and in some places they sow it almost as thin as their corn, for if they should strew the same very thick the ground would become over-rank and choke the corn with weeds. A little before ploughing time, they scatter abroad those beat-boroughs and small sand heaps upon the ground, which afterwards, by the plough's turning down, give heat to the root of the corn. The tillable fields are in some places so hilly that the oxen can hardly take sure footing, in some so tough that the plough will scarcely cut them, and in some so shelfy that the corn hath much ado to fasten his root. The charges of this beating, burning, scoading [scattering] and sanding, ordinarily amounteth to no less than twenty shillings for every acre, which done, the tiller can commonly take but two crops of wheat and two of oats, and then is driven to give it at least seven or eight years leyre [lying, i.e. fallow], and to make his breach elsewhere.

Of wheat there are two sorts, French, which is bearded and requireth the best soil, recompensing the same with a profitable plenty, and not-wheat, so termed because it is unbearded, contented with a meaner earth, and contenting with a suitable gain.

Rye is employed only on those worst grounds which will bear no wheat. Barley is grown into great use of late years, so as now they till a larger quantity in one hundred than was in the whole shire before; and of this, in the dear seasons past, the poor found happy benefit, for they were principally relieved and the labourers also fed by the bread made thereof, whereas otherwise the scarcity of wheat fell out so great that these must have made many hungry meals and those outright have starved. In the westernmost parts of Cornwall they carry their barley to the mill within eight or nine weeks from the time that they sowed it; such an hasty ripening do the bordering seas afford. This increase of barley tillage hath also amended Cornish drink by converting that gain [i.e. the increase? or a misprint for grain?] into malt, which (to the ill relishing of strangers) in former times they made only of oats.

I have been always prone to maintain a paradox, that dearth of corn in Cornwall (for with other shires I will not undertake to meddle) so it go not accompanied with a scarcity, is no way prejudicial to the good of the country, and I am induced thus to think for the reasons ensuing. There are no two trades which set so many hands on work at all times of the year as that one of tillage; the husbandman finding profit herein, is encouraged to bestow pains and charges for enclosing and dressing of waste grounds, which therethrough afterwards become also good for pasture. With the ready money gotten by his weekly selling of corn he setteth the artificer on work, who were better to buy dear bread, being but a part of his meat, and which he countervaileth again by raising the price of his ware, than to sit idly knocking his heels against the wall. Their objection, who fear lest the transporting of much away will leave too little at home,

I answer with this observation: when the price of corn falleth, men generally give over surplus tillage and break no more ground than will serve to supply their own turn; the rest they employ in grazing; wherethrough it falleth out that an ill kerned [with grains not fully formed] or saved harvest soon emptieth their old store and leaveth them in necessity to seek new relief from other places. Whereas on the other side, if through hope of vent [selling] they hold on their larger tillage, this retaineth one year's provision underhand, to fetch in another, which upon such occasions may easily be left at home. And of this, what Cornishman is there that hath not seen the experience?

For fruits, both wild, as whorts, strawberries, and raspies, and 'longing to the orchard, as pears, plums, pear-plums, cherries, mulberries, chestnuts, and walnuts, though the meaner sort come short, the gentlemen step not far behind those of other parts, many of them conceiving like delight to graft and plant, and the soil yielding itself as ready to receive and foster. Yet one special privilege which the nearness to the south, the fitness of some grounds standing upon limestones, the well growing of vines and the pleasant taste of their grapes do seem to grant, I have not hitherto known by any to be put in practice, and that is the making of wines. The trial would require little cost and (perhaps) requite it with great advantage.

For fuel, there groweth generally in all parts great store of furze, of which the shrubby sort is called tame, the better grown French, and in some, good quantity of broom. The east quarters of the shire are not destitute of copsewoods, nor they of (almost) an intolerable price; but in most of the west, either nature hath denied that commodity, or want of good husbandry lost it. Their few parcels yet preserved are principally employed to coaling, for blowing of tin. This lack they supply either by stone coal fetched out of Wales or by dried turfs, some of which are also converted into coal to serve the tinner's turn.

Timber hath in Cornwall, as in other places, taken an universal downfall, which the inhabitants begin now, and shall hereafter rue more at leisure. Shipping, housing, and vessel [casks] have bred this consumption, neither doth any man (wellnear) seek to repair so apparent and important a decay. As for the statute standles, commonly called hawktrees, the breach of the sea and force of the weather do so pare and gall them that they can pass under no better title than scarecrows.

Among creatures of breathing life, I will only note such as minister some particular cause of remembrance.

Touching venomous worms, Cornwall can plead no such charter of nature's exemption as Ireland. The country people retain a conceit that the snakes by their breathing about a hazel wand do make a stone ring of blue colour, in which there appeareth the yellow figure of a snake, and that beasts which are stung, being given to drink of the water wherein this stone hath been soaked, will therethrough recover. There was such an one bestowed on me, and the giver avowed to have seen a part of the stick sticking in it; but *penes authorem fit fides* [the credibility of authors varies]. This mention of snakes called to my remembrance how not long since a merry Cornish gentleman tried that old fable to be no fable, which showeth the dangerous entertaining of such a guest. For he having got one of that kind and broken out his teeth (wherein consisteth his venom) used to carry him about in his bosom, to set him to his mouth, to make him lick his spittle, and when he came among gentlewomen would cast him out suddenly to put them in fear. But in the end their vain dread proved safer than his foolhardiness, for as he once walked alone and was kissing this gentle playfellow, the snake in good earnest, with a stump either newly grown up or not fully pulled out, bit him fast by the tongue, which therewith began so to rankle and swell, that by the time he had knocked this foul player on the head and was come to his place of abode, his mouth was scarce able to contain it. Fain was he therefore to show his mishap, and by gestures to crave aid in earnest of the gentlewoman whom he had aforetime often scared in sport.

Of all manner vermin, Cornish houses are most pestered with rats, a brood very hurtful for devouring of meat, clothes, and writings by day; and alike cumbersome through their crying and rattling, while they dance their gallop galliards in the roof at night.

Strangers, at their first coming into western parts, do complain that they are visited with the slow six-legged walkers, and yet the cleanly homeborn find no such annoyance. It may proceed from some lurking natural effect of the climate, as we read that the travellers who pass the equinoctial do there lose this manlike hunting vermin, and upon their return recover them again.

The other beasts which Cornwall breedeth serve either for venery, or meat, or necessary uses. Beasts of venery, persecuted for their case [fur] or *damage feasance* [trespassing] are martens, squirrels, foxes, badgers, and otters. Profitable for skin and flesh: hares, conies, and deer. The fox planteth his dwelling in the steep cliffs by the seaside, where he possesseth holds so many in number, so dangerous for access, and so full of windings as in a manner it falleth out a matter impossible to disseize him of this his ancient inheritance. True it is, that sometime when he marcheth abroad on foraging, to revictual his *male pardus* [meaning unknown] the captain hunters, discovering his sallies by their espial, do lay their soldierlike hounds, his born enemies, in ambush between him and home, and so with Har and Tue pursue him to the death. Then master Reignard ransacketh every corner of his wily sconce, and bestirreth the utmost of his nimble stumps to quit his coat from their jaws. He crosseth brooks to make them lose the scent, he slippeth into coverts to steal out of sight, he casteth and coasteth the country to get the start of the way, and if he be so met as he find himself overmatched, he abideth and biddeth them battle, first sending the mire of his tail against their eyes in lieu of shot, and then manfully closing at hand-blows with the sword of his teeth, not forgetting yet the whiles to make an honourable retreat with his face still turned towards the enemy; by which means, having once recovered his fortress, he then gives the *fico* [a vulgar gesture] to all that his adversaries can by siege, force, mine, sword, assault, or famine, attempt against him.

The otters, though one in kind, have yet two several places of haunt: some keep the cliffs, and there breed and feed on sea-fish, others live in the fresh rivers and trade not so far down, who being less stored with provision, make bold now and then to visit the land, and to break their fast upon the good man's lambs, or the good wife's poultry.

Of conies, there are here and there some few little warrens, scantily worth the remembering.

Cornwall was stored not long since with many parks of fallow deer, but King Henry VIII, being persuaded (as it is said) by Sir Richard Pollard that those belonging to the Duke could stead him with little pleasure in so remote a part, and would yield him good profit if they were leased out at an improved rent, did condescend to their disparking. So four of them took a fall together, to wit, Cary bullock, Liskerd, Restormel, and Lanteglos. Howbeit, this good husbandry came short of the deviser's promise and the King's expectation, wherethrough the one was shent for the attempt and the other discontented with the effect. Notwithstanding, as Princes' examples are ever taken for warrantable precedents to the subjects, so most of the Cornish gentlemen, preferring gain to delight, or making gain their delight, shortly after followed the like practice, and made their deer leap over the pale to give the bullocks place. Parks yet remaining, are in East Hundred, Poole, Sir Jonathan Trelawny's; newly revived, Halton, Mr Rouse's, lately impaled; and Newton, Mr Corington's, almost decayed. In West Hundred, Boconnock, Sir Reginald Mohun's. In Powder Hundred, Caryhayes, Mr Trevanion's, in Stratton Launcels, Mr Chamond's. In Kerrier Hundred Trelawarren, Mr Vivian's: and Merther, Mr Reskymer's.

Red deer this shire breedeth none, but only receiveth such as in the summer season range thither out of Devon, to whom the gentlemen bordering on their haunt afford so coarse entertainment, that without better pleading their heels, they are fain to deliver up their carcases for a pledge to answer their trespasses.

Beasts serving for meat only are pigs, goats, sheep, and other cattle. For meat, draught, and ploughing, oxen; for carriage and riding, horses; for guard, attendance, and pleasure, dogs of sundry sorts.

What time the shire, through want of good manurance, lay waste and open, the sheep had generally little bodies and coarse fleeces, so as their wool bare no better name than Cornish hair, and for such hath (from all ancientry) been transported without paying custom. But since the grounds began to receive enclosure and dressing for tillage, the nature of the soil hath altered to a better grain, and yieldeth nourishment in greater abundance and goodness to the beasts that pasture thereupon, so as by this means (and let not the owners' commendable industry turn to their surcharging prejudice, lest too soon they grow weary of well doing) Cornish sheep come but little behind the eastern flocks for bigness of mould, fineness of wool, often breeding, speedy fattening, and price of sale, and in my conceit equal, if not exceed them, in sweetness of taste and freedom from rottenness and such other contagions. As for their number, while every dweller hath some, though none keep many, it may sum the total to a jolly rate. Most of the Cornish sheep have no horns, whose wool is finer in quality, as that of the horned more in quantity; yet in some places of the county there are that carry four horns.

The Devon and Somersetshire graziers feed yearly great droves of cattle in the north corner of Cornwall and utter them at home, which notwithstanding, beef, whitsul [dairy produce], leather or tallow bear not any extraordinary price in this county beyond the rate of other places, and yet the opportunity of so many havens tempteth the merchants (I doubt me, beyond their power of resistance) now and then to steal a transportation, and besides, uttereth no small quantity for the revictualling of weather-driven ships. Some gentlemen suffer their beasts to run wild in their woods and waste grounds, where they are hunted and killed with crossbows and pieces in the manner of deer, and by their fierceness and wariness seem to have put on a part of the other's nature. Each ox hath his several name upon which the drivers call aloud, both to direct and give them courage as they are at work.

The Cornish horses commonly are hardly bred, coarsely fed, low of stature, quick in travel, and (after their growth and strength) able enough for continuance, which sort prove most serviceable for a rough and hilly country. But very few of them (through the owner's fault) retain long this their natural goodness, for after two years age they use them to carry sacks of sand, which boweth down and weakeneth their backs, and the next summer they are employed in harrowing, which marreth their pace, two means that so quail also their stomachs and abate their strength as the first rider findeth them overbroken to his hands. Howbeit now, from naught they are almost come to nought, for since the statute, 12 Henry VIII, which enableth every man to seize upon horses that pastured in commons if they were under a certain size, the sheriff's officers, reckoning themselves specially privileged to poll in their master's year, have of late times, whether by his commandment or sufferance, accustomed to drive those waste grounds and to seize on those not voluntary statute-breaking tits [small horses or foals], so as nature denying a great harass and these carrying away the little, it resteth that hereafter, not the dam's foal, but the dam's trotters be trusted unto. This consideration hath made me entertain a conceit that ordinary husbandmen should do well to quit breeding of horses and betake themselves to mules, for that is a beast that will fare hardly, live very long, draw indifferently well, and carry great burdens, and hath also a pace swift and easy enough for their mill and market service. By which means, look what is abated from the usual number of hackneys, should (with a gainful recompense) be added to their goodness; and hereof this quarter hath already taken some experiment: for not long since it happened that one brought over a he ass from France because of the strangeness of the beast (as everything where it comes first serves for a wonder), who following his kind begat many monsters, viz. mules, and for monsters indeed the country people admired them; yea, some were so wise as to knock on the head or give away this issue of his race, as uncouth mongrels.

Amongst living things on the land, after beasts follow birds, who seek harbour on the earth after night, though the air be the greatest place of their haunt by day. Of tame birds, Cornwall hath doves, geese, ducks, peacocks, Guinea ducks, China geese, Barbary hens, and such like. Of wild, quail, rail, partridge, pheasant, plover, snipe, wood-dove, heathcock, powte, &c. But, amongst all the rest, the inhabitants are most beholden to the woodcocks who (when the season of the year affordeth) flock to them in great abundance. They arrive first on the north coast, where almost every hedge serveth for a road, and every plashet [small marshy pool] for springles [snares] to take them; from whence, as the moist places which supply them food begin to freeze up, they draw towards those in the south coast, which are kept more open by the summer's nearer neighbourhood; and when the summer's heat (with the same effect from a contrary cause) drieth up those plashes, nature and necessity guide their return to the northern wetter soil again.

Of hawks there are merlins, sparrowhawks, hobbies, and somewhere lannards. As for the sparrowhawk, though she serve to fly little above six weeks in the year, and that only at the partridge where the falconer and spaniels must also now and then spare her extraordinary assistance, yet both Cornish and Devonshire men employ so much travail in seeking, watching, taking, manning [taming], nuzzling [training to attack prey], dieting, curing, bathing, carrying, and mewing them, as it must needs proceed from a greater folly that they cannot discern their folly herein. To which you may add, their busy, dangerous, discourteous, yea, and sometimes despiteful stealing one from another of the eggs and young ones, who if they were allowed to air naturally and quietly, there would be store sufficient to kill, not only the partridges, but even all the good housewives' chickens in a country.

Of singing birds they have linnets, goldfinches, ruddocks, canary birds, blackbirds, thrushes, and divers other; but of nightingales few or none at all, whether through some natural antipathy between them and the soil (as Pliny writeth, that Crete fostereth not any owls, nor Rhodes eagles, nor Larius Lacus in Italy storks), or rather for that the country is generally bare of covert and wood, which they affect, I leave to be discussed by others.

Not long since, there came a flock of birds into Cornwall about harvest season, in bigness not much exceeding a sparrow, which made a foul spoil of the apples; their bills were thwarted crosswise at the end, and with these they would cut an apple in two at one snap, eating only the kernels. It was taken at first for a foreboden token, and much admired, but soon after notice grew that Gloucestershire and other apple countries have them an over-familiar harm.

In the west parts of Cornwall during the winter season, swallows are found sitting in old deep tin works and holes of the sea cliffs, but touching their lurking places Olaus Magnus maketh a far stranger report; for he saith that in the north parts of the world, as summer weareth out, they clap mouth to mouth, wing to wing, and leg in leg, and so after a sweet singing, fall down into certain great lakes or pools amongst the canes, from whence at the next spring they receive a new resurrection; and he addeth for proof hereof, that the fishermen who make holes in the ice to dip up such fish with their nets as resort thither for breathing, do sometimes light on these swallows congealed in clods of a slimy substance, and that carrying them home to their stoves, the warmth restoreth them to life and flight. This I have seen confirmed by the relation of a Venetian Ambassador employed in Poland, and heard avowed by travellers in those parts, wherethrough I am induced to give it a place of probability in my mind, and of report in this treatise.

After having thus laid open every particular of the land, natural order leadeth my next labour to be employed about the water, and the things incident thereunto. The water I sever into fresh and salt.

Touching fresh water, every hill well-near sendeth forth plentiful, fresh, clear, and pleasant springs, all profitable for moistening the ground, and wholesome for man's use; and divers, by running through veins of metals, supposed also medicinal for sundry diseases; of which more in their particular places. These springs (as several persons assembling make a multitude) take advantage of the falling grounds to unite in a greater strength and beget rivers, which yet are more in number and swifter in course than deep in bottom or extended in largeness; for they work out their bed through an earth full of rocks and stones, suiting therethrough the nature only of some special fishes, of which kind are minnows, shoats, eels, and lampreys. The rest are common to other shires, but the shoat in a manner peculiar to Devon and Cornwall; in shape and colour he resembleth the trout, howbeit in bigness and goodness cometh far behind him; his baits are flies and tag-worms, which the Cornish English-term angle-touches.

Of the rivers and havens which they make, occasion will be ministered us to speak particularly in the next book, and therefore it shall suffice to name the chiefest here in general, which are on the south coast: Tamer, Tavy, Liner, Seaton, Loo, Foy, Fala, Lo; on the north, Camel, Halae.

Of fresh water ponds, either cast out by nature or wrought out by art, Cornwall is stored with very few, though the site of so many narrow valleys offereth many, with the only charge of raising a head. But the ocean's plentiful beams darken the affecting of this petty starlight; touching whose nature and properties, for his saltness in taste, strength in bearing, course in ebbing and flowing, the effects are so well known to the vulgar as they need not any particular relation, and the causes so controverted among the learned as it passeth mine ability to moderate the question. Only this I will note, that somewhat before a tempest, if the sea-water be flashed with a stick or oar, the same casteth a bright shining colour, and the drops thereof resemble sparkles of fire, as if the waves were turned into flames, which the sailors term briny.

Amongst other commodities afforded by the sea, the inhabitants make use of divers creeks for grist-mills, by thwarting a bank from side to side in which a flood-gate is placed with two leaves; these the flowing tide openeth, and after full sea the weight of the ebb closeth fast, which no other force can do, and so the imprisoned water payeth the ransom of driving an under-shoot wheel for his enlargement.

Islands: St Nicholas in the mouth of Plymmouth, St George before Loo, St Michael's Mount, and the Isles of Scilley.

Havens on the south coast are, Plymmouth, Loo, Foy, Falmouth, Helford, and the road of Mount's Bay. On the north, St Ies and Padstowe, of which more hereafter.

Divers of these are daily much endamaged by the earth which the tinners cast up in their working, and the rain floods wash down into the rivers, from whence it is discharged in the havens, and shouldereth the sea out of his ancient possession, or at least encroacheth upon his depth. To remedy this an act of parliament was made, 23 Henry VIII, that none should labour in tinworks near the Devon and Cornish havens; but whether it aimed not at the right cause or hath not taken his due execution, little amendment appeareth thereby for the present, and less hope may be conceived for the future.

Yet this earth, being through such means converted into sand, enricheth the husbandman equally with that of Pactolus: for after the sea hath seasoned it with his salt and fructifying moisture, his waves work up to the shore a great part thereof (together with more of his own store, grated from the cliffs), and the tillers, some by barges and boats, others by horses and wains, do fetch it and therewith dress their grounds. This sand is of divers kinds, colours, and goodness: the kinds, some bigger, some lesser, some hard, some easy. The colours are answerable to the next cliffs. The goodness increaseth as it is taken farther out of the sea.

Some have also used to carry up into their grounds the ooze or salt water mud and found good profit thereby, though not equalling the sand.

To this purpose also serveth orewood, which is a weed either growing upon the rocks under high-water mark, or broken from the bottom of the sea by rough weather and cast upon the next shore by the wind and flood. The first sort is reaped yearly, and thereby bettereth in quantity and quality; the other must be taken when the first tide bringeth it, or else the next change of wind will carry it away. His use serveth for barley land. Some accustomed to burn it on heaps in pits at the cliff-side, and so converted the same to a kind of wood, but the noisome savour hath cursed it out of the country. This flote-ore is now and then found naturally formed like ruffs, combs, and such like, as if the sea would equal us in apparel, as it resembleth the land for all sorts of living creatures.

The sea-strand is also strewed with sundry fashioned and coloured shells, of so diversified and pretty workmanship as if nature were for her pastime disposed to show her skill in trifles. With these are found, moreover, certain nuts, somewhat resembling a sheep's kidney, save that they are flatter; the outside consisteth of a hard dark coloured rind, the inner part of a kernel void of any taste, but not so of virtue, especially for women travailing in child-birth, if at least old wives' tales may deserve any credit. If I become blameworthy in speaking of such toys, Scipio and Laelius shall serve for my patrons, who held it no shame to spend time in their gathering.

But to carry you from these trifles, you shall understand that Cornwall is stored with many sorts of shipping (for that term is the genus to them all), namely, they have cock-boats for passengers, seinboats for taking of pilchard, fisher-boats for the coast, barges for sand, lighters for burden, and barks and ships for traffic; of all which to particularise were *consectari minutias* [to pursue trifles], and therefore I will omit to discourse of them, or of the wrecks proceeding from them, to their great damage and the finder's petty benefit, to whom he that enjoyeth the admiral's right, by the common custom alloweth a moiety for his labour.

But though I shun tediousness herein, I fear I shall breed you nauseam while I play the fishmonger, and yet so large a commodity may not pass away in silence. I will therefore, with what briefness I can, show you what they are, when they come, where they haunt, with what bait they may be trained, with what engine taken, and with what dressing saved.

Herein we will first begin with the peal, trout, and salmon, because they partake of both salt and fresh water, breeding in the one, and living in the other. The trout and peal come from the sea between March and Midsummer, and pass up into the fresh rivers to shed their spawn. They are mostly taken with a hoop-net, made like the eastern weelies [wicker traps], which is placed in the stickelest [most rapid] part of the stream (for there the fish chiefly seek passage) and kept abroad with certain hoops, having his smaller end fastened against the course of the water, and his mouth open to receive the fish while he fareth up by night.

The salmon's principal access is between Michaelmas and Christmas, for then, and not before, the rivers can afford them competent depth, a time forbidden to take them in by the statute 13 Richard II; but if they should be allowed this privilege in Cornwall the inhabitants might utterly quit all hope of good by them for the rest of the year. They are refettest (that is fattest) at their first coming from the sea, and pass up as high as any water can carry them to spawn the more safely, and to that end take advantage of the great rainy floods. After Christmas they return to the sea altogether spent and out of season, whom, as the Spring time cometh on, their fry do follow, and it hath been observed that they (as also the trout and peal) haunt the same rivers where they first were bred. Upon the north coast and to the westward of Foy few or none are taken, either through those rivers' shallowness or their secret dislike. To catch them sundry devices are put in practice: one is with the hook and line, where they use flies for their bait; another, with the salmon spear, a weapon like Neptune's mace, bearded at the points; with this, one standeth watching in the dark night by the deep pools where salmon work their bed for spawning, while another maketh light with a wase [lighted bundle] of reed. The salmon naturally resorteth to the flame, playing in and out, and therethrough is discerned, strooken [struck] and drawn on land by a cord fastened to the spear.

The third and more profitable means of their taking is by hutches. A head of faggots or stones is made across the river and his greatest part let out through a square room therein, whose upper side giveth passage to the water by a grate, but denieth it to the fish, and the lower admitteth his entry through certain thick laths couched slopewise one against another, but so narrowly as he can find no way of return, while the stream tosseth him hither and thither, and the laths' ends gall him if he stumble on the place.

They use also to take salmon and trouts by groping, tickling them under the bellies in the pools where they hover, until they lay hold on them with their hands and so throw them on land. Touching these, one scribbling of the River Liner rhymed as ensueth:

> The storehouse of sun's chevisance,
> The clock whose measures time doth dance,
> The moon's vassal, the lord of chance,
> > Oceanus,
> Ere year's compass his circle end,
> From hugy bosom, where they wend,
> His scaly brood to greet doth send
> > His wife Tellus.
> Some sail but with the coasting shore,
> Some multiply the harbour's store,
> Some far into the river bore,
> > Amongst the rest.
> A threefold rout, of Argus hue,
> Kind to increase, foes to eschew,
> With Lyner's supple mantle blue
> > Themselves revest.

What time, enrich'd by Phoebus' rays,
The alder his new wealth displays
Of budded groats,* and welcome pays
                    Unto the spring,
The trouts of middle growth begin,
And equal peiz'd 'twixt either fin,
At wonted host, Dan Lyner's Inn,
                    Take their lodging.

Next, as the days up early rise,
In comes the peal, whose smaller size,
In his more store and oft supplies
                    A praise doth find.

Lastly, the salmon, king of fish,
Fills with good cheer the Christmas dish,
Teaching that season must relish
                    Each in his kind.

*It is said that the fish cometh when the alder leaf is grown to the breadth of a groat.

And of the salmon in particular:

Now to the Salmon, king of fish, a trice,
Against whose state both skill and will conspire,
Pain brings the fuel, and gain blows the fire,
That hand may execute the head's device.
Some build his house, but his thence issue bar;
Some make his meshy bed, but reave his rest;
Some give him meat, but leave it not digest;
Some tickle him, but are from pleasing far.
Another troop comes in with fire and sword,
Yet cowardly close counterwait his way,
And where he doth in stream mistrustless play,
Veil'd with night's robe, they stalk the shore aboard.
One offers him the daylight in a wase,
As if darkness alone contrived wiles,
But new Neptune, his mate, at land the whiles,
With forked mace dear schools his foolish gaze.
Poor fish, not preying, that art made a prey,

And at thy native home find'st greatest harm;
Though dread warn, swiftness guide, and strength thee arm,
Thy nearness, greatness, goodness, thee betray.

In the haven's great store and divers sort of fish, some at one time of the year and some at another, do haunt the depths and shallows, while the lesser fly the greater, and they also are pursued by a bigger, each preying one upon another, and all of them accustoming once in the year to take their kind of the fresh water. They may be divided into three kinds: shell, flat, and round fish. Of shell fish there are wrinkles, limpets, cockles, mussels, shrimps, crabs, lobsters and oysters.

Of flat fish, rays, thorn-backs, soles, flukes, dabs, plaices.

Of round fish, brit, sprat, barne, smelts, whiting, scad, chad, sharks, cudles [cuttle-fish], eels, conger, basse, mullet, whirlpool [a small whale] and porpoise. The general way of killing these is by weirs, hakings, seins, tucks, and trammels.

The weir is a frith [wattle fence] reaching slopewise through the ooze from the land to low-water mark, and having in it a bunt or cod with an eyehook, where the fish entering upon their coming back with the ebb are stopped from issuing out again, forsaken by the water and left dry on the ooze.

For the haking, certain stakes are pitched in the ooze at low water, athwart from the creek from shore to shore, to whose feet they fasten a net, and at full sea draw the upper part thereof to their stops, that the fish may not retire with the ebb, but be taken as in the weirs.

The sein is a net of about forty fathom in length with which they encompass a part of the sea, and draw the same on land by two ropes fastened at his ends, together with such fish as lighteth within his precinct.

The tuck carrieth a like fashion, save that it is narrower meshed and (therefore scarcely lawful) with a long bunt in the midst. The trammel differeth not much from the shape of this bunt, and serveth to such use as the weir and haking.

The particular taking of sundry kinds of fishes is almost as diverse as themselves. Wrinkles, limpets and mussels are gathered by hand upon the rocks and sands. Many of the crabs breed in the shells of cockles, and of the lobsters in those of wrinkles, as myself have seen: being grown they come forth, and live in holes of rocks, from whence they are dragged out by a long crook of iron.

The shrimps are dipped up in shallow water by the shore side, with little round nets fastened to a staff, not much unlike that which is used for daring of [hypnotising] larks.

The oysters (besides gathering by hand at a great ebb) have a peculiar dredge, which is a thick strong net fastened to three spills of iron, and drawn at the boat's stern, gathering whatsoever it meeteth lying in the bottom of the water, out of which, when it is taken up, they cull the oysters and cast away the residue, which they term gard, and serveth as a bed for the oysters to breed in. It is held that there are of them male and female. The female, about May and June, have in them a certain kind of milk which they then shed, and whereof the oyster is engendered. The little ones at first cleave in great numbers to their mother's shell, from whence, waxing bigger, they wean themselves, and towards Michaelmas fall away. The country people long contained a conceit that in summer time they were out of kind (as indeed the milky are): but some gentlemen making experiment of the contrary began to eat them at all seasons, wherethrough, by spending them oftener and in greater quantity, by spoiling the little ones and by casting away the unseasonable, there ensued a scarcity, which scarcity brought a dearth, the dearth bred a sparing, and the sparing restored a plenty again. They have a property, though taken out of the water, to open against the flood time and to close upon the ebb, or before if they be touched, the which not long since occasioned a ridiculous chance, while one of them through his sudden shutting caught in his own defence three young mice by the heads, that of malice prepensed had conspired to devour him, and so trebled the valour of the cleft block which griped Milo by the hands. Nature hath strewed the shore with such plenty of these shell fishes as thereby she warranted the poor from dread of starving: for every day they may gather sufficient to preserve their life, though not to please their appetite, which, ordinary with us, was miraculous to the Rochellers in their siege 1572.

After shell fish succeed the free fish, so termed because he wanteth this shelly bulwark.

Amongst these, the fluke, sole and plaice follow the tide up into the fresh rivers, where at low water the country people find them by treading, as they wade to seek them, and so take them up with their hands. They use also to pouch them with an instrument somewhat like the salmon-spear.

Of eels, there are two sorts: the one Valsen, of best taste, coming from the fresh rivers, when the great rain floods after September do break their beds and carry them into the sea: the other, bred in the salt water, and called a conger eel, which afterwards, as his bigness increases, ventureth out into the main ocean and is enfranchised a burgess of that vast commonwealth; but in harbour they are taken mostly by spillers made of a cord many fathoms in length, to which divers lesser and shorter are tied at a little distance, and to each of these a hook is fastened with bait: this spiller they sink in the sea where those fishes have their accustomed haunt, and the next morning take it up again with the beguiled fish.

For catching of whiting and basse they use a thread, so named because it consisteth of a long small line with a hook at the end, which the fisherman letteth slip out of his hand by the boat side to the bottom of the water, and feeling the fish caught by the stirring of the line, draweth it up again with his purchase. The porpoises are shaped very big and black. These chase the smaller shoals of fish from the main sea into the havens, leaping up and down in the water, tail after top, and one after another, puffing like a fat lubber out of breath, and following the fish with the flood so long as any depth will serve to bear them; by which means they are sometimes intercepted, for the borderers watching until they be passed far up into some narrow creek, get below them with their boats and cast a strong corded net athwart the stream, with which, and their loud and continual shouting and noise making, they fray and stop them from retiring until the ebb has abandoned them to the hunter's mercy, who make short work with them, and (by an old custom) share them amongst all the assistants with such indifferency, as if a woman with child be present, the babe in her womb is gratified with a portion, a point also observed by the spear-hunters in taking of salmons.

Now from within harbour we will launch out into the deep, and see what luck of fish God shall there send us, which (so you talk not of hares or such uncouth things, for that proves as ominous to the fisherman as the beginning a voyage on the day when Childermas day [Holy Innocents, 28 December] fell, doth to the mariner) may succeed very profitable; for the coast is plentifully stored, both with those foreremembered, enlarged to a bigger size, and divers other, as namely of shell fish, sea hedgehogs, scallops and sheath-fish. Of flat, brits, turbots, dornes, halibut. Round, pilchard, herring, pollock, mackerel, gurnard, illeck [red gurnard], tub [gurnard], bream, oldwife [wrasse], hake, dogfish, lounp [sea-perch?], cunner [gilt-head?], rockling, cod, wrothe [wrasse], becket [sea-bream], haddock, gilthead, rough-hound [dog-fish], squary scad, seal, tunny, and many others, *quos nunc* &c [which now ...]

The sheath, or razor-fish, resembleth in length and bigness a man's finger, and in taste the lobster, but reputed of greater restorative.

The sea hedgehog, of like or more goodness, is enclosed in a round shell, fashioned as a loaf of bread, handsomely wrought and pinked, and guarded by an outer skin of prickles, as the land urchin.

But the least fish in bigness, greatest for gain, and most in number, is the pilchard. They come to take their kind of the fresh (as the rest) between harvest and Allhallowtide, and were wont to pursue the brit, upon which they feed, into the havens, but are now forestalled on the coast by the drovers and seiners. The drovers hang certain square nets athwart the tide, through which the shoal of pilchards passing, leave many behind entangled in the meshes. When the nets are so filled the drovers take them up, cleanse them, and let them fall again.

The seiners complain with open mouth that these drovers work much prejudice to the commonwealth of fishermen, and reap thereby small gain to themselves; for (say they) the taking of some few breaketh and scattereth the whole shoal and frayeth them from approaching the shore; neither are those thus taken merchantable, by reason of their bruising in the mesh. Let the crafts-masters decide the controversy.

The sein is in fashion like that within harbour, but of a far larger proportion. To each of these there commonly belong three or four boats carrying about six men apiece, with which, when the season of the year and weather serveth, they lie hovering upon the coast,and are directed in their work by a balker, or huer, who standeth on the cliff side and from thence best discerneth the quantity and course of the pilchard, according whereunto he cundeth [instructs] (as they call it) the master of each boat (who hath his eye still fixed upon him) by crying with a loud voice, whistling through his fingers, and wheazing certain diversified and significant signs with a bush which he holdeth in his hand. At his appointment they cast out their net, draw it to either hand as the shoal lieth or fareth, beat with their oars to keep in the fish, and at last either close and tuck it up in the sea, or draw the same on land with more certain profit, if the ground be not rough of rocks. After one company have thus shot their net, another beginneth behind them, and a third, as opportunity serveth. Being so taken, some, the country people, who attend with their horses and panniers at the cliff's side in great numbers, do buy and carry home; the larger remainder is by the merchant greedily and speedily seized upon.

They are saved three manner of ways: by fuming, pressing, or pickling, for every of which they are first salted and piled up row by row in square heaps on the ground in some cellar, which they term bulking, where they remain for some ten days until the superfluous moisture of the blood and salt be soaked from them; which accomplished, they rip the bulk and save the residue of the salt for another like service. Then those which are to be ventured for [exported to] France they pack in staunch hogsheads so as to keep them in their pickle. Those that serve for the hotter countries of Spain and Italy they used at first to fume, by hanging them up on long sticks one by one in a house built for the nonce, and there drying them with the smoke of a soft and continual fire, from whence they purchased the name of *fumados*; but now, though the term still remain, that trade is given over, and after they have been ripped out of the bulk, reffed upon sticks, and washed, they pack them orderly in hogsheads made purposely leaky, which afterward they press with great weights, to the end the train may soak from them into a vessel placed in the ground to receive it.

In packing, they keep a just tale of the number that every hogshead containeth, which otherwise may turn to the merchants' prejudice; for I have heard that when they are brought to the place of sale, the buyer openeth one hogshead at adventures; and if he find the same not to answer the number figured on the outside he abateth a like proportion in every other as there wanted in that. The train is well sold, as employed to divers uses, and well-near acquitteth the cost in saving, and the saving setteth almost an infinite number of women and children on work, to their great advantage, for they are allowed a penny for every last's carriage (a last is ten thousand) and as much for bulking, washing, and packing them, whereby a lusty huswife may earn three shillings in a night, for towards the evening they are mostly killed.

This commodity at first carried a very low price, and served for the inhabitants' cheapest provision, but of late times the dear sale beyond the seas hath so increased the number of takers, and the takers' jarring and brawling one with another, and foreclosing the fishes' taking, their kind within harbour, so decreased the number of the taken as the price daily extendeth to a higher rate, equalling the proportion of other fish; a matter which yet I reckon not prejudicial to the commonwealth, seeing there is store sufficient of other victuals, and that of these a twentieth part will serve the country's need, and the other nineteen pass into foreign realms with a gainful utterance.

The seiners' profit in this trade is uncertain, as depending upon the sea's fortune, which he long attendeth and often with a bootless travail, but the pilchard merchant may reap a speedy, large, and assured benefit by dispatching the buying, saving, and selling to the transporters, within little more than three months' space. Howbeit, divers of them snatching at wealth over-hastily, take money beforehand, and bind themselves for the same to deliver pilchards ready saved to the transporter at an under-rate, and so cut their fingers. This venting of pilchards enhanced greatly the price of casks, whereon all other sorts of wood were converted to that use, and yet this scantly supplying a remedy, there was a statute made, 35 Elizabeth, that from the last of June 1594 no stranger should transport beyond the seas any pilchard or other fish in cask unless he did bring into the realm, for every six tons, two hundred of clapboard fit to make cask, and so rateably, upon pain of forfeiting the said pilchard or fish. This act to continue before the next parliament, which hath revived the same, until his (yet not known) succeeder.

The pilchard are pursued and devoured by a bigger kind of fish, called a plusher, being somewhat like the dog-fish, who leapeth now and then above water, and therethrough bewrayeth them to the balker. So are they likewise persecuted by the tunny, and he (though not very often) taken with them *damage faisant*. And that they may no less in fortune than in fashion resemble the flying fish, certain birds called gannets soar over and stoop to prey upon them. Lastly, they are persecuted by the hakes who, not long since, haunted the coast in great abundance, but now, being deprived of their wonted bait, are much diminished, verifying the proverb, 'What we lose in hake we shall have in herring.'

These hakes, and divers of the other forecited, are taken with threads, and some of them with the bolter, which is a spiller of a bigger size. Upon the north coast, where want of good harbours denieth safe road to the fisherboats, they have a device of two sticks filled with corks and crossed flatlong, out of whose midst there riseth a third, and at the same hangeth a sail; to this engine, termed a lestercock, they tie one end of their bolter, so as the wind coming from the shore filleth the sail, and the sail carrieth out the bolter into the sea, which, after the respite of some hours, is drawn in again by a cord fastened at the nearer end. They lay also certain weelies in the sea for taking of cunners [gilt-heads], which therethrough are termed cunner-pots. Another net they have, long and narrow meshed, thwarted with little cords of wide distance, in which the fish entangleth itself and is so drawn up.

For bait they use barne, pilchard, and lugs. The lug is a worm resembling the tagworm [earthworm] or angletouch, and lying in the ooze somewhat deep from whence the women dig them up and sell them to the fishermen; they are descried by their working overhead, as the tagworm. And for lack of other provision the fishermen sometimes cut out a piece of the new taken hake near his tail, and therewith bait their hooks to surprise more of his cannibalian fellows.

The seal, or soyl, is in making and growth not unlike a pig, ugly faced, and footed like a moldwarp; he delighteth in music or any loud noise, and thereby is trained to approach near the shore and to show himself almost wholly above water. They also come on land and lie sleeping in holes of the cliff, but are now and then waked with the deadly greeting of a bullet in their sides.

The fishermen's hooks do not always return them good price, for often there cleaveth to the bait a certain fish like a star, so far from good meat as it is held contagious. There swimmeth also in the sea a round slimy substance called a blobber, reputed noisome to the fish.

But you are tired, the day is spent, and it is high time that I draw to harbour, which good counsel I will follow when I have only told you in what manner the fishermen save the most part of their fish. Some are polled (that is, beheaded), gutted, split, powdered, and dried in the sun, as the lesser sort of hake. Some headed, gutted, jagged and dried, as rays and thornbacks. Some gutted, split, powdered and dried, as buckhorn [dried fish] made of whitings (in the east parts named scalpions), and the smaller sort of conger and hake. Some gutted, split, and kept in pickle, as whiting, mackerel, mullet, bass, peal, trout, salmon, and conger. Some gutted and kept in pickle, as the lesser whitings, pollocks, eels, and squary scads. Some cut in pieces and powdered, as seal and porpoise. And lastly, some boiled and preserved fresh in vinegar, as tunny and turbot.

Besides these floating burgesses of the ocean, there are also certain citizens of the air which prescribe for a corrody [free housing] therein, of whom some serve for food to us, and some but to feed themselves. Amongst the first sort, we reckon the dip-chick (so named of his diving and littleness), coots, sanderling, sea-larks, oxen and kine, sea-pies, puffins, pewits, mews, murres, creysers, curlews, teal, widgeon, burranets, shags, duck and mallard, gull, wildgoose, heron, crane, and barnacle.

These content not the stomach all with a like savouriness, but some carry a rank taste and require a former mortification, and some are good to be eaten while they are young, but nothing toothsome as they grow older. The gulls, pewits, and most of the residue, breed in little desert islands bordering on both coasts, laying their eggs on the grass without making any nests, from whence the owner of the land causeth the young ones to be fetched about Whitsuntide for the first brood, and some weeks after for the second. Some one, but not every such rock, may yield yearly towards thirty dozen of gulls. They are kept tame and fed fat, but none of the sea kind will breed out of their natural place; yet at Caryhayes, Mr Trevanion's house, which bordereth on the cliff, an old gull did (with an extraordinary charity) accustom, for divers years together, to come and feed the young ones (though perhaps none of his alliance) in the court where they were kept.

It is held that the barnacle breedeth under water on such ships' sides as have been very long at sea, hanging there by the bill until his full growth dismiss him to be a perfect fowl, and for proof hereof many little things like birds are ordinarily found in such places, but I cannot hear any man speak of having seen them ripe. The puffin hatcheth in holes of the cliff, whose young ones are thence ferreted out, being exceeding fat, kept salted, and reputed for fish, as coming nearest thereto in their taste. The burranet [sheldrake] hath like breeding, and after her young ones are hatched she leadeth them sometimes overland the space of a mile or better into the haven, where such as have leisure to take their pastime chase them one by one with a boat and stones to often diving, until through weariness they are taken up at the boat's side by hand, carried home, and kept tame with the ducks. The eggs of divers of these fowls are good to be eaten.

Sea-fowl not eatable are gannets, osprey (Pliny's *haliaeetos*). Amongst which, jackdaw (the second slander of our country) shall pass for company, as frequenting their haunt though not their diet. I mean, not the common daw, but one peculiar to Cornwall, and therethrough named a Cornish chough; his bill is sharp, long, and red, his legs of the same colour, his feathers black, his conditions, when he is kept tame, ungracious, in filching and hiding of money and such short ends, and somewhat dangerous in carrying sticks of fire.

After having marched over the land, and waded through the sea, to discover all the creatures therein, insensible and sensible, the course of method summoneth me to discourse of the reasonable, to wit, the inhabitants, and to plot down whatsoever noteworthily belongeth to their estate, real and personal, and to their government, spiritual and temporal. Under their real estate, I comprise all that their industry hath procured, either for private use or intercourse and traffic.

In private life, there cometh into consideration their tenements, which yield them sustenance, and their houses, which afford them a place of abode. Every tenement is parcel of the demesne, or services of some manor.

Commonly thirty acres make a farthing land, nine farthings a Cornish acre, and four Cornish acres a knight's fee.

But this rule is over-ruled to a greater or lesser quantity according to the fruitfulness or barrenness of the soil.

That part of the demesne which appertaineth to the lord's dwelling-house they call his barton, or berton. The tenants to the rest hold the same either by sufferance, will, or custom, or by convention. The customary tenant holdeth at will, either for years or for lives, or to them and their heirs, in divers manners according to the custom of the manor. Customary tenants for life take for one, two, three or more lives, in possession, or reversion, as their custom will bear. Somewhere the wives hold by widows' estate, and in many places, when the estate is determined by the tenant's death, and either to descend to the next in reversion or to return to the lord, yet will his executor or administrator detain the land, by the custom, until the next Michaelmas after, which is not altogether destitute of a reasonable pretence. Amongst other of this customary land there are seventeen manors appertaining to the Duchy of Cornwall, who do every seventh year take their holdings (so they term them) of certain commissioners sent for the purpose, and have continued this use for the best part of three hundred years, through which they reckon a kind of inheritable estate accrued unto them.

But this long prescription notwithstanding, a more busy than well occupied person, not long since, by getting an Exchequer lease of one or two tenements, called the whole right in question, and albeit God denied his bad mind any good success, yet another taking up this broken title, to salve himself of a desperate debt prosecuted the same so far forth as he brought it to the issue of a *nisi prius* [a jury sitting]. Hereon certain gentlemen were chosen and requested by the tenants to become suitors for stopping this gap before it had made an irremediable breach. They repaired to London accordingly, and preferred a petition to the then Lord Treasurer Burleigh. His Lordship called unto him the Chancellor and Coife Barons of the Exchequer [coifs were worn by very senior lawyers], and took a private hearing of the cause. It was there manifestly proved before them, that besides this long continuance and the importance (as that which touched the undoing of more than a thousand persons), her Highness possessed no other lands that yielded her so large a benefit in rents, fines, heriots, and other perquisites. These reasons found favourable allowance, but could obtain no thorough discharge until the gentlemen became suppliants to her Majesty's own person, who, with her native and supernatural bounty, vouchsafed us gracious audience, testified her great dislike of the attempter, and gave express order for stay of the attempt, since which time this barking dog hath been muzzled. May it please God to award him an utter choking, that he never have power to bite again.

Herein we were beholden to Sir Walter Ralegh's earnest writing (who was then in the country), to Sir Henry Killigrew's sound advice, and to Master William Killigrew's painful soliciting (being the most kind patron of all his country and countrymen's affairs at court).

In times past, and that not long ago, holdings were so plentiful and holders so scarce, as well was the landlord who could get one to be his tenant, and they used to take assurance for the rent by two pledges of the same manor. But now the case is altered; for a farm, or (as we call it) a bargain, can no sooner fall in hand than the survey-court shall be waited on with many officers, vying and revying each on other; nay, they are taken mostly at a ground-hop before they fall, for fear of coming too late. And over and above the old yearly rent they will give a hundred or two hundred years' purchase and upward at that rate, for a fine, to have an estate of three lives, which sum commonly amounteth to ten or twelve years' just value of the land. As for the old rent, it carrieth at the most the proportion but of a tenth part to that whereat the tenement may be presently improved, and somewhere much less, so as the parson of the parish can in most cases suspend as much by his tithe, as the lord by his rent. Yet is not this dear setting everywhere alike; for the western half of Cornwall cometh far short of the eastern, and the land about towns exceedeth that lying farther in the country.

The reason of this enhanced price may prove (as I guess) partly for that the late great trade into both the Indies hath replenished these parts of the world with a larger store of the coin-current metals than our ancestors enjoyed, partly because the banishment of single-living votaries, younger marriages than of old, and our long freedom from any sore wasting war or plague, hath made our country very populous, and partly in that this populousness hath enforced an industry in them, and our blessed quietness given scope and means to this industry. But howsoever I aim right or wide at this, once certain it is that for these husbandry matters the Cornish inhabitants are in sundry points swayed by a diverse opinion from those of some other shires. One, that they will rather take bargains at these excessive fines than a tolerable improved rent, being in no sort willing to offer a penny, for they reckon that but once smarting, and this a continual aching; besides, though the price seem very high, yet mostly four years' tillage, with the husbandman's pain and charge, goeth near to defray it. Another, that they fall everywhere from commons to enclosure, and partake not of some eastern tenants' envious dispositions, who will sooner prejudice their own present thrift by continuing this mingle-mangle, than advance the lord's expectant benefit after their term expired. The third, that they always prefer lives before years, as both presuming upon the country's healthfulness, and also accounting their family best provided for when the husband, wife, and child are sure of a living. Neither may I (without wrong) conceal the just commendation of most such wives, in this behalf: namely, when a bargain is so taken to these three, it often falleth out that afterwards the son marrieth, and delivereth his yerving-goods (as they term it) to his father, who in lieu thereof, by his wife's assent, (which in many ancient deeds was formal) departeth to him and his daughter-in-law, with the one half of his holding in hand. Now, though after the father's decease the mother may, during her life, turn them both out of doors, as not bound by her own word, and much less by her husband's, yet I have seldom or never known the same put in practice, but true and just meaning hath ever taken place.

Yet another unconscionable quirk some have of late pried into, viz. in a joint lease to three intended by the taker and payer, to defend successively and entirely, one of them passeth over his interest to a stranger, who by rigour of law shall hold it during the lives of the other twain.

The ordinary covenants of most conventionary tenants are, to pay due capons, do harvest journeys, grind at the mill, sue to the court, discharge the office of reeve and tithingman, dwell upon the tenement, and to set out no part thereof to tillage without the lord's licence first obtained. Which conditions are yet enlarged or restrained according to the demisor's humour.

Usual it is for all sorts of tenants, upon death, at least, if not surrender or forfeiture, to pay their best beast for a heriot [inheritance tax]; yea, if a stranger passing through the country chance to leave his carcass behind him, he must also redeem his burial by rendering his best beast which he hath with him to the lord of the soil; or if he have none, his best jewel; or rather than fail, his best garment then about him in lieu thereof. But this custom hath been somewhat shaken in coming to trial, and laboureth of a dangerous fever, though the Cornish gentlemen use all possible remedies of almost *fas et nefas* [right and wrong/lawful and unlawful], by pleading the eleven points of the law, to keep it on live.

The free tenants' services are ordinary with those of other places, save that they pay in most places only fee-Morton releases, which is after five marks the whole knight's fee (so-called after John, Earl first of Morton, then of Cornwall, and lastly king of this land) whereas that of fee-Gloucester is five pound. And to accomplish this part, I have here inserted a note of the Cornish knights' fees and acres, which I received from my learned and religious kinsman Master Robert Moyle. [Omitted.]

Now to weave on our former web. The ancient manner of Cornish building was to plant their houses low, to lay the stones with mortar of lime and sand, to make the walls thick, their windows arched and little, and their lights inwards to the court, to set hearths in the midst of the room for chimneys, which vented the smoke at a louvre in the top, to cover their planchings with earth, to frame the rooms not to exceed two stories, and the roofs to rise in length above proportion, and to be packed thick with timber, seeking therethrough only strength and warmness;

whereas nowadays they seat their dwellings high, build their walls thin, lay them with earthen mortar, raise them to three or four stories, mould their lights large and outward, and their roofs square and slight, coveting chiefly prospect and pleasure. As for glass and plaster for private men's houses, they are of late years' introduction.

The poor cottager contenteth himself with cob for his walls, and thatch for his covering. As for brick and lath walls, they can hardly brook the Cornish weather, and the use thereof being put in trial by some, was found so unprofitable as it is not continued by any.

It resteth, that after the Cornish inhabitants' real private estate, I speak of their intercourse and traffic, and so step forth to their personal.

This intercourse is obtained by highways and bridges. For highways, the Romans did not extend theirs so far, but those laid out of later times are in the eastern part of Cornwall uneasy, by reason either of their mire or stones, besides many uphills and downhills. The western are better travellable, as less subject to these discommodities: generally the statute 18 Eliz. for their amendment is reasonably well executed.

Bridges, the River Tamer hath Polston, Gresham, Horse, and New Bridge; Lyner, that at Noddeter [Notter]; Seton and Loo, two bridges of the same name; Foy River, Repryn, Lostwithiel, St Nighton or Niot; Fala River, Grampord, Tregny; Loo River Helston. On the north coast, upon Camel, Wade, Dilland and Helland. Upon Devon, Trywarthevy, &c, for they are worth no enquiry.

For maintenance of traffic by buying and selling, there are weekly markets kept: in the Hundred of East, at Saltash, Launceston and Milbrook. In West Hundred at Loo and Liskerd; in Stratton Hundred at the town of the same name. In Lesnewith Hundred at Bottreaux Castle [Boscastle] and Camelford. In Powder Hundred at Foy, Lostwithiel, Grampord, Tregny and Truro. In Trigg Hundred at Bodmin. In Kerier Hundred at Helston and Perin. And in Penwith Hundred at Penzants and at St Ies. Of these, Bodmyn and Launceston are the greatest: this as placed in the broadest, that in the middle part of the county.

Fairs there are many, some which here ensue.

March 13 at Bodmyn, Helston, St Michael's Mount.

April 24 at Loo. 25 at St Columbs, St Probus.

May 1 at Launceston, Perin.

June 11 at Minhinet. 24 at Launceston, Pelint, Probus, St Columbs.

July, on St Marget's Day at St Stephens, St Thomas transl. at Camelford On St James' day at Golsinni, Saltash.

August 1 at St Germaines.

On St Laurence's day at St Laurence.

On the Assumption of Our Lady, at Lalant.

September, on St Matthew's Day at Liskerd, on St Bartholomew's at Lostwithiel, on the nativity of Our Lady at Kellington, St Mary Week and Marcastow.

October, on St Dionysius' Day at Trevenna in Tintagel.

November, on St Katherine's Day at St Thomas.

On St Leonard's Day at Launceston and Tregny.

December, on St Nicholas' Day at Bodmyn.

And because traffic cannot be exercised without weights and measures, a word or two of them.

Touching weights, the statute 12.H.VII which made a general ordinance therein did specially exempt those appertaining to the coinage, in Devon and Cornwall, viz, that they should be privileged to continue their former usage.

In measures the shire varieth, not only from others, but also in itself, for they have a land-measure and a water-measure; the water-measure, of things sold at the ship's side (as salt and peason) by the inhabitants, is sixteen gallons the bushel, by strangers eighteen and twenty-four. The land-measure differeth in divers places from eighteen to twenty-four gallons the bushel, being least in the eastern parts, and increasing to the westwards, where they measure oats by the hogshead.

The justices of the peace have oftentimes endeavoured to reduce this variance to a certainty of double Winchester [Winchester had a widely recognised standard, of 8 gallons to the bushel]: but though they raised the lower, they cannot abate the higher to this proportion: and yet from the want of this reformation there ensue many inconveniences: for the farmer that hath the greatest bushel at the market maketh a price for the lesser to follow with little (or at least no) rateable deduction. Besides, they sell at home to their neighbours, the rest of the week, by the smaller measure as was paid in the market for the bigger.

There are also some engrossers, who buy wheat of the husbandman after 18 gallons the bushel and deliver it to the transporting merchant for the same sum at 16.

So doth their perch exceed that of other countries, which amounteth unto eighteen foot. And it is likewise observed by strangers that the Cornish miles are much longer than those about London, if at least the weariness of their bodies (after so painful a journey) blemish not the conjecture of their minds. I can impute this general enlargement of saleable things to no cause sooner than the Cornish man's want of vent and money, who therethrough, to equal others in quality of price, is driven to exceed them in quantity of measure.

Touching the personal estate of the Cornish inhabitants, to begin with their name in general, I learn by Master Camden (who, as the arch-antiquary, Justus Lipsius testifieth of him, *Britanniae nebulas claro ingenii sole illustravit* [By the brilliant sun of his genius he throws light on the clouds of Britain] that Ptolemy calleth them *Damnonii*, Strabo *Ostidamnii*, and Aretemidorus *Cossini*.

Touching their particular denominations; where the Saxons have not intruded their newer usances, they partake in some sort with their kinsmen the Welsh; for as the Welshmen catalogize ap Rice, ap Griffin, ap Owen, ap Tuder, ap Lewellin, &c. until they end in the highest of the stock whom their memory can reach unto, so the western Cornish, by a like but more compendious manner, entitle one another with his own and his father's Christian name, and conclude with the place of his dwelling; as, John the son of Thomas dwelling at Pendarvis, is called John Thomas Pendarvis. Richard, his younger brother, is named Richard Thomas Pendarvis, &c. Through which means divers gentlemen and others have changed their names by removing their dwellings, as Trengove to Nance, Bonithon to Carclew, two brethren of the Thomases, the one to Carnsew, the other to Rescrowe, and many other.

Most of them begin with Tre, Pol, or Pen, which signify a town, a top, and a head: whence grew the common by-word:

By Tre, Pol, and Pen,
You shall know the Cornishmen.

Neither do they want some signification, as Godolfin, alias Godolghan, a white eagle: Chiwarton, the green castle on the hill: which gentlemen give such arms. Reskimer, the great dog's race, who beareth a wolf passant. Carnsew, alias Carndew, a black rock, his house Bokelly, which soundeth the lost goat, and a goat he beareth for his coat. Carminow, a little city, Cosowarth, the high grove, &c.

And as the Cornish names hold an affinity with the Welsh, so is their language deduced from the same source, and differeth only in the dialect. But the Cornish is more easy to be pronounced, and not so unpleasing in sound, with throat letters, as the Welsh.

A friend of mine, one Master Thomas Williams, discoursed once with me that the Cornish tongue was derived from, or at least had some acquaintance with the Greek, and besides divers reasons which he produced to prove the same, he vouched many words of one sense in both, as for example:

Greek	Cornish	English
Teino	Tedna	Draw
Mamma	Mamm	Mother
Episcopos	Escoppe	Bishop
Klyo	Klowo	Hear
Didaskein	Dathisky	To teach
Kyon	Kye	Dog
Kentron	Kentron	Spur
Methyo	Methow	Drink
Scaphe	Schapth	Boat
Ronchos	Ronchie	Snorting, &c.

This language is stored with sufficient plenty to express the conceits of a good wit, both in prose and rhyme; yet can they no more give a Cornish word for *tie*, than the Greeks for *ineptus*, the French for *stand*, the English for *emulus*, or the Irish for *knave*.

Oaths they have not past two or three natural, but are fain to borrow of the English; marry, this want is relieved with a flood of most bitter curses and spiteful nicknames.

They place the adjective after the substantive, like the Grecians and Latins, as *paz agan*, father ours, *march guiddu*, horse white, &c.

In numbering they say, Wonnen 1, Deaw 2, Tre 3, Pidder 4, Pimp 5, Whey 6, Zith 7, Eath 8, Naw 9, Deag 10, Ednack 11, Dowthack 12, Tarnack 13, Puzwarthack 14, Punthack 15, Wheytack 16, Zitack 17, Itack 18, Naunzack 19, Eygganz 20, Deaw Eigganz 40, Cans 100, Mille 1000, Molla 10,000.

Durdatha why, is Good morrow to you. *Ternestatha*, Good night. *Fatlughan a why?*, How do you do? *Da durdalatha why*, Well, I thank you.

Betha why lawanneck, Be you merry. *Benetugana*, Farewell. A sister they call *whoore*: a whore, *whorra*: a priest, *coggaz*: a partridge, *grigear*: a mare, *cazock*. *Relauta*, By my troth. *Warra fay*, By my faith. *Molla tuenda laaz*, Ten thousand mischiefs in thy guts. *Mille vengeance warna thy*, A thousand vengeances take thee. *Pedn joll*, Devil's head. *Pedn brauze*, Great head. *Pedn mowzack*, Stinking head, and so *in infinitum*. Which terms notwithstand-ing, though they witness their spite on the one side, yet retain they as great a proof of their devotion on the other; for the Lord's Prayer, the Apostles' Creed, and the Ten Commandments have been used in Cornish beyond all remembrance. But the principal love and knowledge of this language lived in Dr Kenall the civilian [Doctor of Civil Law], and with him lieth buried, for the English speech doth still encroach upon it and hath driven the same into the uttermost skirts of the shire. Most of the inhabitants can [know] no word of Cornish, but very few are ignorant of the English; and yet some so affect their own as to a stranger they will not speak it, for if meeting them by chance you inquire the way or any such matter, your answer shall be, *Meea navidna cowza sawzneck*, 'I can speak no Saxonage'. The English which they speak is good and pure, as receiving it from the best hands of their own gentry and the eastern merchants, but they disgrace it in part with a broad and rude accent, somewhat like the Somersetshire men, especially in pronouncing the names: as, Thomas they call *Tummas* and *Tubby*; Matthew, *Mathaw*; Nicholas, *Nichlaaz*; Reignald, *Reinol*; David, *Daavi*; Mary, *Maari*; Frauncis, *Frowncis*; James, *Jammez*; Walter, *Watty*; Robert, *Dobby*; Rafe, *Raw*; Clemence, *Clemmowe*, &c. holding herein a contrary course of extension to the Italians' abridge-ment, who term Francis, *Cecco*; Dominick, *Beco*; Lawrence, *Renzo*: as also to the Turks, who name Constantinople, *Stampoli*; Adrianople, *Adrina*; an Olifant, *Fil*; and the Sicilians, who curtail Nicholas to *Cola*.

Besides these, they have taken up certain peculiar phrases which require a special dictionary for their interpretation, of which kind are: 'Tis not *bezib'd* (that is, fortuned) to me; Thou hast no *road* (aim); He will never *scrip* (escape) it; He is nothing *pridy* (handsome): as also *boobish* (lubberly), *dule* (comfort), *lidden* (by-word), *shune* (strange), *thew* (threaten), *skew* (shun), *hoase* (forbear).

To reprove one of laziness they will say, 'Dost thou make idle a coat?' that is, a coat for idleness. In conjecturing what number may effect a thing, they add, 'or some', as: two, or some; ten, or some; twenty, or some; *id est*, 'thereabouts'.

The other rude terms wherewith Devon and Cornishmen are often twitted may plead in their defence not only the prescription of antiquity but also the title of propriety and the benefit of significancy, for most of them take their source from the Saxon, our natural language, and continue in use amongst the Dutch, as nimme commeth of nimpt: vang, of fieng: the one importing a taking by oneself: the other by delivery, both of which we now confound. Ich to ick, cund to cundigen, lading to Geladen: erving goods to Erbnuss, so 'thwyting' is properly the cutting of little chips from a stick, 'pilme' the dust which ariseth, 'brusse' that which lieth; which terms, as they express our meaning more directly, so they want but another Spenser to make them passable.

The number of Cornish inhabitants, though it cannot directly be summed, may yet proportionably be guessed at by the musters taken of the able men (hereafter set down), which we will value at a third part of the whole, in ensuing Bodin's rate. [Bodin was a French statistician, by whose formula the population of Cornwall in 1600 would have been around 40,000.]

But another question falleth sometimes into scanning, namely, whether Cornwall have heretofore been better stored with people than it is now. Some hold the affirmative, and vouch to prove it the general decay of inland towns, where whole streets, besides particular houses, pay tribute to Comedown Castle, as also the ruins yet resting in the wild moors, which testify a former inhabitance. Others incline again to the negative, alleging the reasons heretofore touched, in the dear price of farms or bargains, by which my assent is rather swayed; for I suppose that those waste grounds were inhabited and manured when the Saxons' and Danes' continual invasions drove them to abandon the sea-coast, save in such towns as were able to muster, upon any sudden occasion, a sufficient number for their own defence. The residue retired into the heart of the land, where upon a longer warning they might sooner assemble from all sides to make head, and the enemy in so far a march and retreat should adventure a greater hazard to be distressed by the way; which policy the French were driven unto in Edward III's time upon the Englishmen's often roads, and the Spaniards make use of at this day in their Indies. Touching the decayed inland towns, they are countervailed with a surplusage of increase of those on the coast, and the desolate walls in the moors have begotten a sevenfold race of cottages near the sea side.

And thus much of Cornwall compared with itself. Now if you match it with other champian [unenclosed] shires, methinks, I may gather the same to be better inhabited within a like circuit of miles, because the plenty of hills and valleys afford a larger quantity of ground thereunto. He that cannot conceive this may read Polybius in his ninth book, where it is written that for this reason Lacedemon, being but forty-eight furlongs in compass, containeth more dwellings than Megalopolis, which extendeth unto fifty. My last proof is grounded on this, that where the most part of the shire is severed into enclosures, you cannot easily make choice to stand in any one of them above a quarter of a mile distance from some dwelling-house.

After the names, language, and number thus perused, the Cornish people's disposition and quality of mind and body, as well ancient as present, and then their degrees and recreations succeed to be surveyed. The first inhabitants, or aborigines, as the paynims held, resembled those whom our stories affirm Brute to have found here at his landing, huge of body, rough of living, and savage of conditions; whom an old poet deciphered in certain verses, which I received of my particular kind friend and generally well-deserving countryman, Mr Camden, now Clarentieulx, which he since hath published:

> *Titanibus illa*
> *Sed paucis famulosa domus, quibus uda ferarum*
> *Terga dabant vestes, cruor haustus, pocula trunci:*
> *Antra lares, dumeta thoros, coenacula rupes,*
> *Praeda cibos, raptus venerem, spectacula cades,*
> *Imperium vires, animos furor, impetus arma,*
> *Mortem pugna, sepulchra rubos, monstrique gemebat*
> *Monticolis tellus, sed eorum plurima tractus,*
> *Pars erat Occidui, terro maiorque premebat,*
> *Te furor extremum Zephiri Cornubia limen.*

Which sound thus in English:

> This was the Titans' haunt, but with
>   No plenty did abound,
> Whom beasts' raw hides for clothing serv'd,
>   For drink, the bleeding wound;

Cups, hollow trees; their lodging, dens;
  Their beds, brakes; parlour, rocks;
Prey, for their food; ravine, for lust;
  Their games, life-reaving knocks.
Their empire, force; their courage, rage;
  A headlong brunt, their arms;
Combat, their death; brambles, their grave.
  The earth groan'd at the harms
Of these mount-harbour'd monsters; but
  The coast extending west
Chief foison had, and dire dismay,
  And sorest fury prest
Thee, Cornwall, that with utmost bound
  Of Zephyr art possest.

But afterwards the Cornishmen, through the conversation of foreign merchants trading into their country for tin, by the testimony of Diodorus Siculus, grew to a larger measure of civility than others their fellow but more remote islanders. From which civility, in the fruitful age of canonization, they stopped a degree farther to holiness and helped to stuff the church calendar with divers saints, either made or born Cornish. Such was Keby, son to Solomon Prince of Cornwall; such Peran who (if my author, the legend, lie not) after that (like another *Johannes de temporibus*) he had lived two hundred years with perfect health, took his last rest in a Cornish parish, which therethrough he endowed with his name. And such were Dubslane, Machecu, and Manslunum, who (I speak upon Matthew of Westminster's credit) forsook Ireland, thrust themselves to sea in a boat made of three ox skins and a half, with seven days' victuals, and miraculously arrived in Cornwall.

Of Cornishmen, whose industry in learned knowledges hath recommended their fame to posterity, these few as yet are only come to my notice.

John of Cornwall, a student at Rome, and other places in Italy, wrote of the Incarnation of Christ, against Peter Lumbard, and dedicated the same to Pope Alexander III, by whom he was highly favoured.

Simon Thurnay, after he had outgone all the Oxford scholars in profane learning (saith the commendable painful antiquary, and my kind friend, Master Hooker), passed from thence to Paris, and there so profited in the study of divinity that he attained the chiefest place amongst the profound Sorbonists. But it was a windy knowledge that thus filled his sails of glory, which grew at last so as to tempest his wits, as he held Aristotle superior to Moses and Christ, and yet but equal to himself But this extreme surquedry [arrogance] forfeited his wits, so as at last they could not serve him to know any letter in the book, or to remember ought that he had done.

In King Henry III's time lived Michael of Cornwall, admirable (as those days gave) for his variety of Latin rhymes, who maintained the reputation of his country against Henry de Abrincis, the King's Archpoet, but somewhat angerly [laboriously] as it seemeth by these verses against the said Abrincis:

> *Est tibi gamba capri, crus Passeris & latus apri,*
> *Os leporis, catuli nasus, dens et gena muli,*
> *Frons vetulae, tauri caput & color undique Mauri*
> *His argumentis, quibus est argutia mentis,*
> *Quod non a Monstro differs, satis hic tibi monstro.*

> Gamb'd like a goat, sparroe thigh'd, side as boar
> Hare-mouthed, dog nos'd, like mule thy teeth and chin,
> Browed as old wife, bull-headed, black as Moor.
> If such without, then what are you within?
> By these my signs, the wise will easily conster
> How little thou dost differ from a monster.

Walter of Exon, a Franciscan friar of Carocus in Cornwall, at the request of Baldwin of Exon, (de-)formed the History of Guy of Warwick.

Godfrey, surnamed of Cornwall, was about that time a cunning schoolman, and Divinity Reader in Paris.

William de Grenefild, from the Deanery of Chichester, stepped to the Chancellorship of England and Archbishopric of York, under King Edward I.

In Edward II's days, one Geffrey of Cornwall is remembered for a writer. John Trevisa, a Cornishman, lived in Richard II's reign and translated divers books into English.

King Henry I, not unmindful of the civiller arts among his martial exploits, founded a University at Caen in Normandy and appointed Michael Tregury of Cornwall, for his rare gifts in learning, to be

Governor thereof. In Henry VI's time, John Skewish compiled certain abridgements of chronicles, and the wars of Troy.

King Henry VII promoted John Arundel for his learning to the see of Exeter.

Neither is Thomas Trivet to be forgotten as a writer, though he have graven his memory in a fairer letter by building the costly bridge at Bridgewater, of which sometime he was Lord.

Within our remembrance Cornwall hath bred or harboured divines, graced with the degree of Doctorship, Moreman, Tremayn, Nichols and Rolls. Bachelors, Medhope, Stowel, Moore, Denis. Of preachers the shire holdeth a number, plentiful in regard of other shires, though not competent to the full necessity of their own, all commendably labouring in their vocation, though not endowed with an equal ability to discharge the same.

In the civil law there lived of late Dr. Kennal, and now doth Dr. Carew, one of the ancientest masters of the Chancery; in which calling, after his younger years spent abroad to his benefit, he hath reposed himself. Bachelors there are, Carnsew, Kete, and Denis. Barristers at the common law, Chiverton, Tremayne, Skawn, Michel, Moyle, Courtnay, Tub, Treffry, Sayer. These testify the honesty of their carriage by the mediocrity of their estate: and (if they will give me leave to report a jest) do verify an old gentleman's prophecy, who said that there stood a man at Polston bridge (the first entrance into Cornwall as you pass towards Launceston where the assizes are holden) with a black bill in his hand, ready to knock down all the great lawyers that should plant themselves in that county. In earnest, whether it be occasioned through the country's poverty, or by reason of the far distance thereof from the supremer courts, or for that the multiplicity of petty ones near at hand, appertaining to the Duchy, Stannary, and franchises, do enable the attorneys and such like of small reading to serve the people's turn and so curtail the better studied counsellors' profiting, once certain it is that few men of law have, either in our time or in that of our forefathers, grown here to any supereminent height of learning, livelihood, or authority.

Of like fortune, but less number, are the physicians; by how much the fewer, by so much the greater witnesses of the soil's healthfulness. The most professors of that science in this country, saving only one, John Williams, can better vouch practice for their warrant, than warrant for their practice. Amongst these I reckon Rawe Clyes, a blacksmith by his occupation, and furnished with no more learning than is suitable to such a calling, who yet hath ministered physic for many years, with so often success and general applause, that not only the homebred multitude believeth mightily in him, but even persons of the better calling resort to him from remote parts of the realm to make trial of his cunning, by the hazard of their lives; and sundry, either upon just cause, or to cloak their folly, report that they have reaped their errand's end at his hands.

But far more commendable is Mr Atwel, sometimes parson of Calverly in Devon, and now of St Tue [St Ewe] in Cornwall: for besides other parts of learning with which he hath been seasoned, he is not unseen in the theorics of physic, and can out of them readily and probably discourse touching the nature and accidents of all diseases. Besides, his judgment in urines cometh little behind the skilfullest in that profession. Marry, his practice is somewhat strange, and varying from all others, for though now and then he use blood-letting, and do ordinarily minister *manus Christi* [sugar and rose-water] and such like cordials of his own compounding (a point fitting well with my humour, as enabling nature who best knoweth how to work), yet mostly for all diseases he prescribeth milk, and very often milk and apples, a course deeply subject to the exception of the best esteemed practitioners; and such notwithstanding, as whereby either the virtue of the medicine, or the fortune of the physician, or the credulity of the patient, hath recovered sundry out of desperate and forlorn extremities.

This his reputation is of many years' standing, and maintaineth itself unimpaired. But the same soareth to a higher pitch by the help of another wing, and that is, his liberality. On the poor he bestoweth his pains and charges gratis; of the rich he taketh moderately, but leaves the one half behind in gift amongst the household, if he be called abroad to visit any; the rest, together with the profits of his benefice (rather charitably accepted than strictly exacted from his parishioners), he poureth out with both hands *in pios usus* [for pious purposes], and will hardly suffer a penny to sleep, but never to dwell with him.

Few towns there are in Cornwall, or any other shire between that and London, which have not in some large measure tasted of his bounty. None cometh in kindness to see him, but departeth gratified with somewhat, if his modesty will accept it. Briefly, his sound affection in religion is so waited on by honesty of life and pleasantness of conversation, that in Fabricius's voluntary poverty he is an equal partner of his honour, and possesseth a large interest in the love of his neighbours. My love to virtue, and not any particular beholdingness, hath expressed this my testimony.

For persons employed in state affairs, and therethrough stept to preferment, that I may not outstride late remembrance, Sir Richard Edgecumb the elder was Comptroller of the household and Privy Counsellor to King Henry VII, being sent by him also in divers embassies, in one of which, to the Duke of Brittany, he deceased.

King Henry VIII made like use in this last kind of John Tregonwel, who, graduated a Doctor and dubbed a knight, did his prince good service and left fair revenues to his posterity.

Sir Thomas Arundel, a younger brother of Lanhearn House, married the sister to Queen Katherine Howard, and in Edward VI's time was made a Privy Counsellor, but cleaving to the Duke of Somerset, he lost his head with him.

Sir Henry Killigrew, after embassies and messages, and many other employments of peace and war in his Prince's service, to the good of his country, hath made choice of a retired estate, and reverently regarded by all sorts, placeth his principal contentment in himself, which, to a life so well acted, can no way be wanting.

Master George Carew in his younger years gathered such fruit as the university, the inns of court, and foreign travel could yield him; upon his return he was first called to the bar; then supplied the place of secretary to the Lord Chancellor Hatton; and after his decease performed the like office to his two successors, by special recommendation from her Majesty, who also gave him the Protonotaryship of the Chancery, and in *anno* 1598 sent him Ambassador to the King of Poland and other northern potentates, where, through unexpected accidents he underwent extraordinary perils, but God freed him from them and he performed his duty in acceptable manner, and at this present the commonwealth useth his service as a Master of the Chancery.

Cornwall, no doubt, hath afforded a far larger proportion of well deserving and employed members, to the good of their Prince and country; albeit they fall not within the compass of my knowledge, and it is likely that the succeeding age will much increase the number by means of her Highness's bounty, who to that end hath established seed-plots of free schools, with competent pensions out of her own coffers for the teachers at Saltash, Launceston, and Perin, three market towns of the county.

In descending to martial men, Arthur claimeth the first mention, a Cornishman by birth, a King of Britain by succession, and the second of the three Christian worthies by desert, whom (if you so please) that captain of arms and venery, Sir Tristram, shall accompany. From them I must make a great leap (which convinceth me an unworthy associate of the antiquary college) to Sir John Naphant, who (if I mistake not) was by country a Cornishman, though by inhabitance a Calisian [inhabitant of Calais, then an English colony], where Henry VII used his service in great trust, and Cardinal Wolsey owned him for his master. More assured I am that Sir John Arundell of Trerice, upon a long fight at sea, took prisoner one Duncane Camel, a hardy Scottish pirate, and presented him to King Henry VIII, for our chroniclers report it. Towards the end of that King's reign, Sir William Godolphin also demeaned himself very valiantly in a charge which he bare beyond the seas, as appeared by the scars he brought home, no less to the beautifying of his fame than the disfiguring of his face: whose nephew, of the same name and dignity, hath so enriched himself with sufficiency for matters of policy by his long travel, and for martial affairs by his present valiant carriage in Ireland, that it is better known how far he outgoeth most others in both, than easily to be discerned, for which he deserveth principal commendation himself.

So did Sir Richard Greinvile the elder interlace his home magistracy with martial employments abroad, whereof the King testified his good liking by his liberality. Which domestical example encouraged his son Roger the more hardily to hazard, and the more willingly to resign his life in the unfortunate *Mary Rose*, a disposition and success equally fatal to that house, for his son again, the second Sir Richard, after his travel, and following the wars under the Emperor Maximilian against the great Turk, for which his name is recorded by sundry foreign writers, and his undertaking to people Virginia and Ireland, made so glorious a conclusion in her Majesty's ship, the *Revenge* (of which he had charge as Captain, and of the whole fleet as Vice-Admiral), that it seemed thereby, when he found none other to compare withal in his life, he strived through a virtuous envy to exceed it in his death: a victorious loss for the realm, and of which the Spaniard may say with Pirrhus, that many such conquests would beget his utter overthrow. Lastly, his son John took hold of every martial occasion that was ministered him, until, in service against her Highness' enemies under the command of Sir Walter Ralegh, the ocean became his bed of honour.

Neither may I without wrong pass over Captain George Wray in silence, who (by a rare temperature of virtues) breathed courage into his soldiers, purchased love amongst his acquaintance and bred dismay in his enemies. Or Captain Hender, the absolutest man of war for precise observing martial rules which his days afforded, besides his commendable sufficiency of head and hand for invention and execution. I will end with Master William Lower, late captain of Sir Frauncis Vere's company in Netherland, who hath opened the war school unto a great many Cornish young gentlemen, that under his conduct sought to conform themselves unto his pattern, every way accomplished with all due parts of honour.

For mechanical sciences, the old Veale of Bodmyn might justly expostulate with my silence if I should not spare him a room in this Survey while he so well deserves it. This man hath been so beholden to Mercury's predominant strength in his nativity, that without a teacher he is become very skilful in well-near all manner of handicrafts: a carpenter, a joiner, a millwright, a free-mason, a clockmaker, a carver, metal-founder, architect, & *quid non?* [what isn't he?] yea a surgeon, physician, alchemist, &c. so as that which Gorgias of Leontium vaunted of the liberal sciences he may profess of the mechanical, viz. to be ignorant in none.

The Cornish minds thus qualified, are the better enabled to express the same by the strong, active, and healthful constitution of their bodies; touching each whereof a little in particular, though we shall have a fitter general occasion to discourse thereof where we handle their pastimes. For strength, one John Bray (well known to me as my tenant) carried upon his back, at one time, by the space wellnear of a buttlength, six bushels of wheaten meal, reckoning fifteen gallons to the bushel, and the miller, a lubber of four and twenty years age, upon the whole.

John Romane, a short clownish grub, would bear the whole carcass of an ox, and yet never tugged with him, like that so famous Milo, when he was a calf.

For activity, one Kiltor, committed to Launceston gaol for the last Cornish commotion, lying there in the castle-green upon his back threw a stone of some pounds' weight over that tower's top which leadeth into the park.

For health, 80 and 90 years age is ordinary in every place, and in most persons accompanied with an able use of the body and his senses. One Polzew, lately living, reached unto 130; a kinsman of his to 112; one Beaxchamp to 106; yea, Brawne the beggar, a Cornishman by wandering (for I cannot say by inhabitance) though Irish by birth, outscoreth a hundred winters by I wot not how many revolutions. And in the parish where God hath seated my poor dwelling, I remember the decease of four, within fourteen weeks space, whose years added together made up the sum of 340.

Now to the degrees of their several callings, wherein as I will post over the Dukes to another place, so for noblemen I may deliver in a word, that Cornwall at this present enjoyeth the residence of none at all. The occasion whereof groweth partly because their issue female have carried away the inhabitance, together with the inheritance, to gentlemen of the eastern parts, and partly for that their issue male, little affecting so remote a corner, liked better to transplant their possessions nearer to the heart of the realm. Elder times were not so barren: for besides the Lord Tregoyes in William Conqueror's days, Bottreaux Castle vaunteth his Baron of that title, both now descended to the Earls of Huntingdon; the last deceased of which, retaining the honour, departed with the land to my kind friend Master John Hender, a gentleman for his good parts, employed by her Majesty amongst others in the peace government of the shire.

The Lord Bonvile his house was at Trelawne, alias Trelawney, lately purchased of her Highness by Sir Jonathan Trelawny, a knight well spoken, staid in his carriage, and of thrifty providence.

The Lord Bray dwelt at [gap in text]: the Lord Brooke at Kellington, where one of them hath his tomb: the Lord Marney at Colquite: and the Lord Denham at Cardenham.

Boconnock also appertained to the Earls of Devon, and was by Frauncis Earl of Bedford sold to Sir William Mohun, who derived his pedigree from the ancient barons of that name, and is also issued from one of those Earls of Devon's sisters and heirs. This, together with other fair possessions, now resteth in Sir Reignald Mohun, his son, one that by his courteous, just, and liberal course of life, maintaineth the reputation, and increaseth the love always borne his ancestors.

The most Cornish gentlemen can better vaunt of their pedigree than their livelihood, for that they derive from great antiquity (and I make question whether any shire in England, of but equal quantity, can muster a like number of fair coat-armours), whereas this declineth to the mean. One cause there is of both, proceeding from the want of those supplies which service, law, and merchandise afford the more inward inhabitants of the realm, as I have elsewhere touched. Yet this rule is not so general but that it admitteth his exceptions, for there are divers whose patrimonies extend to a large proportion, and for the residue, the cheapness of their provisions and their casualties of tin and fines (which two latter ordinarily treble the certain revenue of their rents), enable them with their few scores to equal the expenses of those eastern dwellers who reckon by the hundreds. Besides, they find means by a survey to defray any extraordinary charge of building, marriage, lawing, or such like. Yet I cannot deny but that some, in gaping for dead men's shoes, find their improvident covetous humour punished with going barefoot.

This angle which so shutteth them in, hath wrought many interchangeable matches with each other's stock, and given beginning to the proverb, that all Cornish gentlemen are cousins; which endeth in an injurious consequence, that the King hath there no cousins. They keep liberal, but not costly builded or furnished houses, give kind entertainment to strangers, make even at the year's end with the profits of their living, are reverenced and beloved of their neighbours, live void of factions amongst themselves (at leastwise such as break out into any dangerous excess) and delight not in bravery of apparel; yet the women would be very loath to come behind the fashion in newfangledness of the manner, if not in costliness of the matter, which perhaps might overempty their husbands' purses. They converse familiarly together, and often visit one another. A gentleman and his wife will ride to make merry with his next neighbour, and after a day or twain those two couples go to a third, in which progress they increase like snowballs, till through their burdensome weight they break again.

And here I thought requisite to lay down the names of such Cornish gentlemen as I find recorded to have come in with the Conqueror, and now residing in Cornwall.

I had also made a more painful than perfect collection of most of the Cornish gentlemen's names and arms. But because the publishing thereof might perhaps go accompanied with divers wrongs, to my much reverenced friends the heralds by thrusting my sickle into their harvest, to a great many my countrymen whom my want of information should be forced to pass over unmentioned, and to the truth itself where my report (relying upon other men's credits) might through their error intitle me the publisher (though not the author) of falsehood, I rather thought fit altogether to omit it, and to note only, that of divers gentlemen there have been in Cornwall, either their names are worn out or their livings transferred by the females into other families, as likewise, sundry of those there now inhabiting are lately denized Cornish, being generally drawn thither (besides other more private respects) through either the desire of change, which the disease of discontent affecteth, or the love of quiet in so remote a corner, or the supposal of commodities there arising and accruing, or the warranties from overlooking and bearing where little difference in quality tendeth to an equality in estates.

From gentility we will descend to civility, which is, or should be in the townsmen. Those in Cornwall do no more by nature, than others elsewhere by choice, conceive themselves an estranged society from the upland dwellers, and carry, I will not say a malice, but an emulation against them, as if one member in a body could continue his wellbeing without a beholdingness to the rest. Their chiefest trade consisteth in uttering their petty merchandises and artificers' labours at the weekly markets. Very few among them make use of that opportunity, which the site upon the sea proffereth unto many, for building of shipping and trafficking in gross, yet some of the eastern towns piddle that way, and some others give themselves to fishing voyages, both which (when need requireth) furnish her Majesty's navy with good store of very serviceable mariners.

There are (if they be not slandered) that hunt after a more easy than commendable profit, with little hazard, and (I would I could not say) with less conscience. *Anno* 32 Henry VIII, an Act of Parliament was made for repairing, amongst others, the Borough towns of Launceston, Liskerd, Lostwithiel, Bodmyn, Truro and Helston in Cornwall, but what fruit to their good I cannot relate.

Within late years' memory the sea coast towns begin to proclaim their bettering in wealth by costly increase of buildings; but those of the inland, for the most part, vouch their ruined houses and abandoned streets as too true an evidence that they are admitted no partners in this amendment. If I mistake not the cause, I may with charity enough wish them still the same fortune, for as is elsewhere touched, I conceive their former large peopling to have been an effect of the country's impoverishing, while the invasion of foreign enemies drove the seacoast inhabitants to seek a more safe than commodious abode in those inland parts.

Strangers occasioned to travel through the shire were wont, no less sharply than truly, to inveigh against the bad drink, coarse lodging, and slack attendance which they found in those houses that went for inns, neither did their horses' better entertainment prove them any welcomer guests than their masters; but instead of remedy they received in answer, that neither such an outcorner was frequented with many wayfarers, nor by hanging out of signs or forestalling at the town's end, like the Italians, did they invite any; and to make great provision upon small hope of utterance were to incur a scorn-worthy loss, seeing *Aspettare, & non venire* (saith the same Italian) is one of the *tre cose da morire*. [To wait in vain is one of the three things that cause death.]

Touching the yeomanry of Cornwall, I can say little worth the observing for any difference from that of other shires, and therefore I will step down the next stair to husbandman.

These in times not past the remembrance of some yet living, rubbed forth their estate in the poorest plight; their grounds lay all in common, or only divided by stitch-meal [in small, widely separated holdings]: little bread-corn: their drink water, or at best but whey, for the richest farmer in a parish brewed not above twice a year, and then, God wot what liquor: their meat, whitsul, as they call it, namely milk, sour milk, cheese, curds, butter, and such like as came from the cow and ewe, who were tied by the one leg at pasture: their apparel coarse in matter, ill shapen in manner: their legs and feet naked and bare, to which sundry old folk had so accustomed their youth that they could hardly abide to wear any shoes, complaining how it kept them over hot. Their horses shod only before, and for all furniture a pad and halter, on which the meaner country wenches of the western parts do yet ride astride, as all other English folk used before Richard II's wife brought in the side-saddle fashion of straw.

Suitable hereunto was their dwelling, and to that their implements of household: walls of earth, low thatched roofs, few partitions, no planchings or glass windows, and scarcely any chimneys other than a hole in the wall to let out the smoke: their bed, straw and a blanket; as for sheets, so much linen cloth had not yet stepped over the narrow channel between them and Brittany. To conclude, a mazer and a pan or two comprised all their substance; but now most of these fashions are universally banished, and the Cornish husbandman conformeth himself with a better supplied civility to the eastern pattern, which hath directed him a more thriving form of husbandry, and our halcyon days of peace enabled him to apply the lesson, so as, his fine [down-payment on taking the lease] once overcome, he can maintain himself and his family in a competent decency to their calling, and findeth money to bestow weekly at the markets for his provisions of necessity and pleasure; for his quarterly rent serveth rather as a token of subjection to his landlord, than any grievous exaction on his tenement.

One point of their former roughness some of the western people do yet still retain, and therethrough in some measure verify that testimony which Matthew of Westminster giveth of them together with the Welsh, their ancient countrymen, namely, how fostering a fresh memory of their expulsion long ago by the English, they second the same with a bitter repining at their fellowship; and this the worst sort express in combining against and working them all the shrewd turns which with hope of impunity they can devise. Howbeit, it shooteth not to a like extremity in all places and persons, but rather by little and little weareth out unto a more mild and conversable fashion. Amongst themselves they agree well, and company lovingly together; to their gentlemen they carry a very dutiful regard, as inured in their obeisance from their ancestors, and holding them as roytelets [petty kings] because they know no greater. Only it might be wished that divers amongst them had less spleen to attempt lawsuits for petty supposed wrongs, or not so much subtlety and stiffness to prosecute them; so should their purses be heavier and their consciences lighter: a reporter must aver no falsehood, nor conceal any truth.

We must also spare a room in this Survey to the poor, of whom few shires can show more, or own fewer, than Cornwall. Ireland prescribeth to be the nursery, which sendeth over yearly, yea and daily, whole shiploads of these crooked slips, and the dishabited towns afford them rooting; so upon the matter, the whole county maketh a contribution to pay those lords their rent. Many good statutes have been enacted for redress of these abuses, and upon the first publishing, heedfully and diligently put in practice; but after the nine days' wonder expired, the law is forgotten, the care abandoned, and those vermin swarm again in every corner. Yet those peevish charitable cannot be ignorant that herethrough, to the high offence of God and good order, they maintain idleness, drunkenness, theft, lechery, blasphemy, atheism, and, in a word, all impiety, for a worse kind of people than these vagabonds the realm is not pestered withal; what they consume in a day will suffice to relieve an honest poor parishioner for a week, of whose work you may also make some use. Their starving is not to be feared, for they may be provided for at home if they list; no alms should therefore be cast away upon them, to the robbery of the needy impotent, but money least of all, for in giving him silver you do him wrong by changing his vocation, while you metamorphose him from a beggar to a buyer. Lacks he meat, drink, or apparel? (and nothing else he ought to be owner of): he must procure them of the worst by free gift, and not make choice, for a just price, of the best. Well, though the rogue laugh you to scorn at night, the ale-wife hath reason the next day to pray for you.

Surely we find by experience, that this so heinous an enormity may be both easily and quickly reformed; for let the constables execute upon the rogues that last most beneficial Act of Parliament with due severity for one week, and the terror thereof will free the parish for a month: use it a month, and you are acquitted for the whole year. If the constables persist in their remissness, let the justices lay the penalty upon them, and they will no longer hoodwink themselves at their neighbours' faults. Let the neighbour be so pinched by the purse but once or twice, and he will become a great deal the more sensible to season his charity with discretion for a long time after.

Upon the first statute, there was a house of correction erected at Bodmin, to the great charge but little credit of the country; which experience lessoneth them to elude this latter, by appointing certain cottagers' houses in every parish to serve *nomine tenus* [deemed to be a prison], for that purpose.

Lazar-houses, the devotion of certain Cornish gentlemen's ancestors erected at Minhinet by Liskerd, St Thomas by Launceston, and St Laurence by Bodmyn, of which this last is well endowed and governed. Concerning the other I have little to say, unless I should echo some of their complaints, that they are defrauded of their right. The much eating of fish, especially newly taken, and therein principally of the livers, is reckoned a great breed of those contagious humours which turn into leprosy;

but whence soever the cause proceedeth, daily events minister often piti-
ful spectacles to the Cornishmen's eyes of people visited with this afflic-
tion some being authors of their own calamity, by the forementioned diet
and some others succeeding therein to an *haereditarius morbus* [hereditary
illness] of their ancestors: whom we will leave to the poorest comfort in
misery, a helpless pity.

But let me lead you from these unpleasing matters, to refresh yourselves
with taking view of the Cornishmen's recreations, which consist principally in feasts and pastimes.

Their feasts are commonly harvest dinners, church-ales, and the solem-
nizing of their parish church's dedication, which they term their saint's
feast.

The harvest dinners are held by every wealthy man, or as we term it,
every good liver, between Michaelmas and Candlemas, whereto he
inviteth his next neighbours and kindred; and though it bear only the
name of a dinner, yet the guests take their supper also with them, and
consume a great part of the night after in Christmas rule. Neither doth
the good cheer wholly expire (though it somewhat decrease) but with the
end of the week.

For the church-ale, two young men of the parish are yearly chosen by
their last foregoers [predecessors] to be wardens, who dividing the task,
make collection among the parishioners of whatsoever provision it pleas-
eth them voluntarily to bestow. This they employ in brewing, baking, and
other acates [provisions], against Whitsuntide, upon which holidays the
neighbours meet at the church-house and there merrily feed on their own
victuals, contributing some petty portion to the stock, which by many
smalls groweth to a meetly greatness, for there is entertained a kind of
emulation between these wardens, who by his graciousness in gathering
and good husbandry in expending, can best advance the church's profit.
Besides, the neighbour parishes at those times lovingly visit one another,
and this way frankly send their money together. The afternoons are consumed in such exercises as old and young folk (having leisure) do accustomably wear out the time withal.

When the feast is ended, the wardens yield in their account to the
parishioners, and such money as exceedeth the disbursements is laid up in
store to defray any extraordinary charges arising in the parish, or imposed
on them for the good of the country or the prince's service, neither of

which commonly gripe so much but that somewhat still remaineth to cover the purse's bottom.

The saint's feast is kept upon the dedication day by every house-holder of the parish, within his own doors, each entertaining such foreign acquaintance as will not fail, when their like turn cometh about, to requite him with the like kindness.

Of late times many ministers have, by their earnest invectives, both condemned these saints' feasts as superstitious, and suppressed the church-ales as licentious, concerning which, let it breed none offence for me to report a conference that I had not long since with a near friend, who (as I conceive) looked hereinto with an indifferent and unprejudicating eye.

I do reverence (said he) the calling and judgement of the Ministers, especially when most of them concur in one opinion, and that the matter controversed holdeth some affinity with their profession. Howbeit, I doubt lest in their exclaiming or declaiming against church ales and saints' feasts, their ringleaders did only regard the rind and not pierce into the pith, and that the rest were chiefly swayed by their example, even as the vulgar rather stooped to the weight of their authority than became persuaded by the force of their reasons. And first touching church-ales, these be mine assertions, if not my proofs: of things induced by our forefathers, some were instituted to a good use and perverted to a bad; again, some were both naught in the invention and so continued in the practice. Now that church-ales ought to be sorted in the better rank of these twain may be gathered from their causes and effects, which I thus raise up together: entertaining of Christian love, conforming of men's behaviour to a civil conversation, compounding of controversies, appeasing of quarrels, raising a store which might be converted partly to good and godly uses, as relieving all sorts of poor people, repairing of churches, building of bridges, amending of highways, and partly for the prince's service, by defraying at an instant such rates and taxes as the magistrate imposeth for the country's defence. Briefly, they tend to an instructing of the mind by amiable conference, and an enabling of the body by commendable exercises.

But I, fearing lest my friend would run himself out of breath in this volubility of praising, stept athwart him with these objections: that he must pardon my dissenting from his opinion touching the goodness of the institution, for taken at best it could not be marshalled with the sacred matters, but rather with the civil, if not with the profane; that the very title of ale was somewhat nasty, and the thing itself had been corrupted with such a multitude of abuses, to wit, idleness, drunkenness, lasciviousness, vain disports of minstrelsy, dancing, and disorderly night-watchings, that the best curing was to cut it clean away. As for his fore-remembered good causes and effects, I saw not but that if the people's minds were guided by the true level of Christian charity and duty, such necessary and profitable contributions might still be continued gratis, and the country eased of that charge to their purse and conscience, which ensueth this gormandise.

His reply was, that if this ordinance could not reach unto that sanctity which dependeth on the first table, yet it succeeded the same in the next degree, as appertaining to the second. Mine exception against the title he mockingly matched with their scrupulous preciseness, who (forsooth) would not say Christmas nor Michaelmas as other folk did, but Christ's-tide and Michael's-tide, who (quoth he) by like consequence must also bind themselves to say Tom's-tide, Lam'stide, and Candle's-tide. But if the name of ale relish so ill, whereas the liquor itself is the Englishman's ancientest and wholesomest drink, and serveth many for meat and cloth too, he was contented I should call it church-beer or church-wine, or what else I listed; marry, for his part he would *loqui cum vulgo* [speak like the common people], though he studied *sentire cum sapientibus* [to think like the wise]. Where I affirmed that the people might by other means be trained with an equal largess to semblable works of charity, he suspected lest I did not enter into a thorough consideration of their nature and quality, which he had observed to be this: that they would sooner depart with twelve-pennyworth of ware than sixpence in coin, and this shilling they would willingly double so they might share but some pittance thereof again. Now in such indifferent matters, to serve their humours for working them to a good purpose could breed no manner of scandal. As for the argument of abuse which I so largely dilated, that should rather conclude a reformation of the fault than an abrogation of the fact.

For to prosecute your own metaphor (quoth he) surely I hold him for a sorry surgeon that cannot skill to salve a sore but by taking away the limb, and little better than the physician who, to help the disease, will reave the life of his patient from him. Abuses, doubtless, great and many have by success of time crept hereinto, as into what other almost, divine or civil, do they not? And yet in these public meetings they are so presented to every man's sight as shame somewhat restraineth the excess, and they may much the sooner be both espied and redressed. If you think I go about to defend church-ales with all their faults, you wrong your judgment, and your judgment wrongeth me. I would rather (as a burgess of this ale-parliament) enact certain laws, by which such assemblies should be governed; namely, that the drink should neither be too strong in taste, nor too often tasted; that the guests should be interlarded, after the Persian custom, by ages, young and old, distinguished by degrees of the better and meaner, and severed into sexes, the men from the women; that the meats should be sauced with pleasant but honest talk; that their songs should be of their ancestors' honourable actions; the principal time of the morning I would have hallowed to God's service, the afternoons to man-like activities, and yet I would not altogether bar sober and open dancing until it were first thoroughly banished from marriages, Christmas revels, and (our country's pattern) the court; all which should be concluded with a reasonable and seasonable portion of the night. And so (said he) will I conclude this part of my speech with adding only one word more for my better justification: that in defending feasts, I maintain neither paradox nor conceit *in nubibus* [in clouds, veiled] but a matter practised amongst us from our eldest ancestors with profitable and well pleasing fruit, and not only by our nation, but both in former ages, by the best and strictest disciplined commonwealth of the Lacedemonians, who had their ordinary *syssitia*, and now in our days, as well by the reformed as Catholic Switzers, who place therein a principal *arcanum imperii* [state mystery].

Now touching the saints' feasts, if you taint them with suspect of superstition because they are held upon those saints' days, by whose names the parish churches are styled, I will ward that blow with the shield of Arch-Saint Austine's authority, who in his eighth book of *God's City*, and twenty-seventh chapter, in the like case justifieth a less allowable practice of the primitive Christians. *Summa* [in short], he closed his discourse with this protestation, that he appealed not from, but to the honourably respected censure of the reverend ministry, desiring his speech might receive, not the allowance of a position, but the licence of a proposition; which my friend's modest submission I could not but embrace myself, and recommend it over to your favourable acceptation.

My last note touching these feasts tendeth to a commendation of the guests, who (though rude in their other fashions) may, for their discreet judgment in precedence and presence, read a lesson to our civilest gentry. Amongst them at such public meetings, not wealth but age is most regarded, so as (save in a very notorious disproportion of estates) the younger rich reckoneth it a shame sooner than a grace to step or sit before the elder honest, and rather expecteth his turn for the best room by succession than intrudeth thereto by anticipation.

Pastimes to delight the mind, the Cornish men have gwary miracles, and three men's songs: and for exercise of the body, hunting, hawking, shooting, wrestling, hurling and such other games.

The gwary miracle, in English, a miracle play, is a kind of Interlude, compiled in Cornish out of some scripture history, with that grossness which accompanied the Romans' *vetus comedia* [Old Comedy]. For representing it, they raise an earthen amphitheatre in some open field, having the diameter of his enclosed plain some forty or fifty foot. The country people flock from all sides, many miles off, to hear and see it, for they have therein devils and devices to delight as well the eye as the ear.

The players con not their parts without book, but are prompted by one called the ordinary, who followeth at their back with the book in his hand, and telleth them softly what they must pronounce aloud. Which manner once gave occasion to a pleasant conceited gentleman of practising a merry prank; for he undertaking (perhaps of set purpose) an actor's room, was accordingly lessoned (beforehand) by the ordinary, that he must say after him. His turn came: quoth the ordinary, 'Go forth man, and show thyself.' The gentleman steps out upon the stage, and like a bad clerk in scripture matters, cleaving more to the letter than the sense, pronounced these words aloud. 'Oh,' says the fellow softly in his ear, 'you mar all the play.' And with this his passion the actor makes the audience in like sort acquainted. Hereon the prompter falls to flat railing and cursing in the bitterest terms he could devise; which the gentleman with a set gesture and countenance still soberly related, until the ordinary, driven at last into mad rage, was fain to give over all; which truce, though it brake off the interlude, yet defrauded not the beholders, but dismissed them with a great deal more sport and laughter than twenty such gwaries could have afforded.

They have also three men's songs, cunningly contrived for the ditty, and pleasantly for the note.

Amongst bodily pastimes, shooting carrieth the preeminence; to which in mine younger years I carried such affection, as I induced Archery, persuading others to the like liking, by this ensuing prosopopeia: 'My dear friends, I come to complain upon you, but to yourselves; to blame you, but for your good; to expostulate with you, but in the way of reconciliation. Alas, what my desert can justify your abandoning my fellowship, and hanging me thus up, to be smoke-starved over your chimneys? I am no stranger unto you, but by birth your countrywoman, by dwelling your neighbour, by education your familiar. Neither is my company shameful, for I haunt the light and open fields, nor my conversation dangerous: nay, it shields you from dangers, and those not the least, but of greatest consequence, the dangers of war. And as in fight I give you protection, so in peace I supply you pastime; and both in war and peace, to your limbs I yield active pliantness, and to your bodies healthful exercise; yea, I provide you food when you are hungry, and help digestion when you are full. Whence then proceedeth this unkind and unusual strangeness? Am I heavy for burden? Forsooth, a few light sticks of wood. Am I cumbrous for carriage? I couch a part of myself close under your girdle, and the other part serveth as a walking-staff in your hand. Am I unhandsome in your sight? Every piece of me is comely, and the whole keepeth an harmonical proportion. Lastly, am I costly to be provided, or hard to be maintained? No, cheapness is my purveyor, easiness my preserver; neither do I make you blow away your charges with my breath, or taint your nose with my scent, nor defile your face and fingers with my colour, like that hell-born murderer, whom you accept before me. I appeal then to your valiant princes, Edwards and Henries; to the battles of Cressy, Poitiers, Agincourt, and Flodden; to the regions of Scotland, France, Spain, Italy, Cyprus, yea, and Jewry, to be umpires of this controversy; all which (I doubt not) will with their evidence plainly prove, that when mine adverse party was yet scarcely born, or lay in her swathling clouts, through me only, your ancestors defended their country, vanquished their enemies, succoured their friends, enlarged their dominions, advanced their religion, and made their names fearful to the present age, and their fame everlasting to those that ensue. Wherefore, my dear friends, seeing I have so substantially evicted the right of my cause, conform your wills to reason, conform your reason to practice, and convert your practice to the good of yourselves and your country. If I be praiseworthy, esteem me; if necessary, admit me; if profitable, employ me; so shall you revoke my death to life, and show yourselves no degenerate issue of such honourable progenitors.'

And thus much for Archery, whose tale, if it be disordered, you must bear withal, for she is a woman, and her mind is passionate.

And to give you some taste of the Cornishmen's former sufficiency that way, for long shooting, their shaft was a cloth yard, their pricks [targets] twenty-four score [480 feet, 160 yards]; for strength they would pierce any ordinary armour, and one Master Robert Arundell (whom I well knew) could shoot twelve score, with his right hand, with his left, and from behind his head.

Lastly, for near and well-aimed shooting, butts made them perfect in the one, and roving in the other; for pricks, the first corrupter of archery, through too much preciseness, were then scarcely known, and little practised. And in particular, I have heard by credible report of those who professed and protested themselves to have been eyewitnesses, that one Robert Bone of Antony shot at a little bird sitting upon his cow's back, and killed it, the bird (I mean) not the cow; which was either very cunning in the performance, or very foolish in the attempt. The first of these somewhat resembled one Menelaus, mentioned by Zosimus, Book 2, who notching three arrows and shooting them all at once, would strike three several persons, and might have deserved a double stipend in the Grand Signior's guard, where the one half of his archers are left-handed, that they may not turn their tail to their Sultan while they draw. The other may in some sort compare with that Avo, reported by Saxo Grammaticus for so good a marksman, as with one arrow he clave the string of his adversary's bow, the second he fixed between his fingers, and with the third struck his shaft which he was notching: or with that exploit of the father's piercing an apple on his son's head, attributed by the same Saxo to one Toko, a Dane, and by the Switzers' histories to Guillaum Tell, the chief occasioner and part author of their liberty.

Hurling taketh his denomination from throwing of the ball, and is of two sorts: in the east parts of Cornwall to goals, and in the west to the country.

For hurling to goals, there are fifteen, twenty, or thirty players, more or less, chosen out on each side, who strip themselves into their slightest apparel, and then join hands in rank one against another. Out of these ranks they match themselves by pairs, one embracing another, and so pass away, every of which couple are specially to watch one another during the play.

After this, they pitch two bushes in the ground some eight or ten foot asunder, and directly against them, ten or twelve score off, other twain in like distance, which they term their goals. One of these is appointed by lots to the one side, and the other to his adverse party. There is assigned for their guard a couple of their best stopping hurlers; the residue draw into the midst between both goals, where some indifferent person throweth up a ball, the which whosoever can catch and carry through his adversary's goal hath won the game. But therein consisteth one of Hercules his labours, for he that is once possessed of the ball hath his contrary mate waiting at inches, and assaying to lay hold upon him. The other thrusteth him in the breast with his closed fist to keep him off, which they call butting, and place in well doing the same no small point of manhood.

If he escape the first, another taketh him in hand, and so a third, neither is he left, until having met (as the Frenchman says) *chaussure à son pied* ['a shoe to fit', i.e. met his match], he either touch the ground with some part of his body in wrestling, or cry Hold, which is the word of yielding. Then must he cast the ball (named dealing) to some one of his fellows, who catching the same in his hand, maketh away withal as before, and if his hap or agility be so good as to shake off or outrun his counter-waiters, at the goal he findeth one or two fresh men ready to receive and keep him off. It is therefore a very disadvantageable match or extraordinary accident that loseth many goals; howbeit, that side carrieth away best reputation which giveth most falls in the hurling, keepeth the ball longest, and presseth his contrary nearest to their own goal. Sometimes one chosen person on each party dealeth the ball.

The hurlers are bound to the observation of many laws, as that they must hurl man to man, and not two set upon one man at once: that the hurler against the ball must not butt, nor hand-fast under girdle: that he who hath the ball must butt only in the other's breast: that he must deal no fore-ball, viz. he may not throw it to any of his mates standing nearer the goal than himself. Lastly, in dealing the ball, if any of the other part can catch it flying between, or ere the other have it fast, he thereby winneth the same to his side, which straightway of defendant becometh assailant, as the other of assailant falls to be defendant. The least breach of these laws the hurlers take for a just cause of going together by the ears, but with their fists only, neither doth any among them seek revenge for such wrongs or hurts, but at the like play again. These hurling matches are mostly used at weddings, where commonly the guests undertake to encounter all comers.

The hurling to the country is more diffuse and confuse [disorderly], as bound to few of these orders. Some two or more gentlemen do commonly make this match, appointing that on such a holiday they will bring to such an indifferent place, two, three, or more parishes of the east or south quarter, to hurl against so many other of the west or north. Their goals are either those gentlemen's houses, or some towns or villages three or four miles asunder, of which either side maketh choice, after the nearness to their dwellings. When they meet there is neither comparing of numbers nor matching of men, but a silver ball is cast up, and that company which can catch and carry it by force or sleight to their place assigned, gaineth the ball and victory. Whosoever getteth seizure of this ball findeth himself generally pursued by the adverse party, neither will they leave till (without all respects) he be laid flat on God's dear earth, which fall once received disableth him from any longer detaining the ball; he therefore throweth the same (with like hazard of intercepting, as in the other hurling) to some one of his fellows farthest before him, who maketh away withal in like manner. Such as see where the ball is played give notice thereof to their mates, crying Ware east, Ware west, &c. as the same is carried.

The hurlers take their next way over hills, dales, hedges, ditches, yea, and thorough bushes, briars, mires, plashes, and rivers what-soever, so as you shall sometimes see twenty or thirty lie tugging together in the water, scrambling and scratching for the ball. A play (verily) both rude and rough, and yet such as is not destitute of policies, in some sort resembling the feats of war; for you shall have companies laid out before on the one side, to encounter them that come with the ball, and of the other party to succour them, in manner of a fore-ward. Again, other troops lie hovering on the sides, like wings to help or stop their escape, and where the ball itself goeth, it resembleth the joining of the two main battles; the slowest footed who come lag, supply the show of a rear-ward; yea, there are horsemen placed also on either party (as it were in ambush) and ready to ride away with the ball if they can catch it at advantage. But they may not so steal the palm, for gallop any one of them never so fast, yet he shall be surely met at some hedge corner, cross-lane, bridge, or deep water, which (by casting the country) they know he must needs touch at, and if his good fortune guard him not the better, he is like to pay the price of his theft with his own and his horse's overthrow to the ground. Sometimes the whole company runneth with the ball seven or eight miles out of the direct way which they should keep. Sometimes a footman getting it by stealth, the better to scape unespied, will carry the same quite backwards, and so at last get to the goal by a windlass, which once known to be won, all that side flock thither with great jollity, and if the same be a gentleman's house they give him the ball for a trophy, and the drinking out of his beer to boot.

The ball in this play may be compared to an infernal spirit, for whosoever catcheth it fareth straightways like a madman, struggling and fighting with those that go about to hold him, and no sooner is the ball gone from him but he resigneth this fury to the next receiver, and himself becometh peaceable as before. I cannot well resolve whether I should more commend this game for the manhood and exercise, or condemn it for the boisterousness and harms which it begetteth; for as on the one side it makes their bodies strong, hard, and nimble, and puts a courage into their hearts to meet an enemy in the face, so on the other part it is accompanied with many dangers, some of which do ever fall to the players' share. For proof whereof, when the hurling is ended, you shall see them retiring home as from a pitched battle, with bloody pates, bones broken and out of joint, and such bruises as serve to shorten their days; yet all is good play, and never attorney nor coroner troubled for the matter.

Wrestling is as full of manliness, more delightful, and less dangerous; which pastime either the Cornishmen derive from Corineus, their first pretended founder, or (at least) it ministered some stuff to the farcing of that fable. But to let that pass, their continual exercise in this play hath bred them so skilful an habit, as they presume that neither the ancient Greek *Palaestritae* nor the Turks' so much delighted *Pelrianders*, nor their once countrymen and still neighbours, the Bretons, can bereave them of this laurel; and matchless, certes, should they be if their cunning were answerable to their practice, for you shall hardly find an assembly of boys in Devon or Cornwall where the most untowardly amongst them will not as readily give you a muster of this exercise, as you are prone to require it. For performing this play, the beholders cast themselves in a ring,. which they call making a place, into the empty middle space whereof the two champion wrestlers step forth, stripped into their doublets and hosen, and untrussed that they may so the better command the use of their limbs, and first shaking hands in token of friendship they fall presently to the effects of anger; for each striveth how to take hold of other with his best advantage, and to bear his adverse party down, wherein, whosoever overthroweth his mate in such sort as that either his back, or the one shoulder and contrary heel do touch the ground, is accounted to give the fall. If he be endangered, and make a narrow escape, it is called a foil. This hath also his laws, of taking hold only above girdle, wearing a girdle to take hold by, playing three pulls for trial of the mastery, the fall-giver to be exempted from playing again with the taker, and bound to answer his successor, &c.

Many sleights and tricks appertain hereunto, in which a skilful, weak man will soon get the overhand of one that is strong and ignorant. Such are the trip, fore-trip, inturn, the faulx, forward and backward, the mare, and divers other like.

Amongst Cornish wrestlers now living, my friend John Goit may justly challenge the first place, not by prerogative of his service in her Majesty's guard, but through having answered all challenges in that pastime without blemish. Neither is his commendation bounded within these limits, but his clean made body and active strength extend (with great agility) to whatsoever other exercise of the arm or leg, besides his ability (upon often trial) to take charge at sea, either as master or captain. All which good parts he graceth with a good fellowlike, kind, and respectful carriage.

Silver prizes for this and other activities were wont to be carried about by certain *circumforanei* [itinerant traders] or set up for bidales [benefit matches]; but time, or their abuse, hath now worn them out of date and use.

The last part of this first book is to plot down the Cornish government, which offereth a double consideration: the one, as an entire state of itself; the other, as a part of the realm; both which shall be severally handled.

Cornwall, as an entire state, hath at divers times enjoyed sundry titles: of a kingdom, principality, duchy, and earldom, as may appear by these few notes, with which I have stored myself out of our Chronicles.

If there was a Brute, King of Britain, by the same authority it is to be proved that there was likewise a Corineus, Duke of Cornwall, whose daughter Gwendolene, Brute's eldest son Locrine took to wife, and by her had issue Madan, that succeeded his father in the kingdom.

Next him I find Henninus Duke, who married Gonorille, one of King Leir's daughters and heirs, and on her begat Morgan: but whiles he attempted with his other brother-in-law to wrest the kingdom from their wives' father by force of arms, before the course of nature should cast the same upon them, Cordeilla, the third disherited sister, brought an army out of France to the old man's succour, and in a pitched battle bereft Henninus of his life.

Clotenus King of Cornwall begat a son named Mulmutius Dunwallo who, when this land had long been distressed with the civil wars of petty kings, reduced the same again into one peaceable monarchy. Belinus, brother to that great terror to the Romans Brennus, had for his appaunage, as the French term it, Loegria, Wales and Cornwall.

Cassibelane, succeeding his brother Lud in the kingdom, gave to his son Tennancius the Duchy of Cornwall, after this island became a parcel of Julius Caesar's conquests, the same rested itself, or was rather vexed a long time, under the government of such rulers as the Romans sent hither. But the Britons, turning at last their long patience into sudden fury, rose in arms, slew Alectus, the Emperor Diocletian's deputy, and inserted their leader Asclepiodotus Duke of Cornwall, with the possession of the kingdom.

Conan Meridock, nephew to Octavius, whom the Emperor Constantine appointed governor of this island, was Duke of Cornwall.

At the Synod of Arles in France there was present one Corineus, son to Salomon Duke of Cornwall.

After the above-named Octavius' decease, Maximianus, a Roman, who married his daughter, succeeded him also in government; between whom and the foreremembered Conan grew great wars, which concluding at last in peace, Maximianus passed with an army into France, conquered there Armorica (naming it little Britain) and gave the same in fee to Conan, who being once peaceably settled wrote over unto Dionethus or Dionotus Duke or King of Cornwall (as Matthew of Westminster termeth him) to send him some maidens, whom he might couple in marriage with his people; whereon St Ursula and her companions the 11,000 virgins were shipped and miscarried, as their well known history reporteth.

Nicholas Gille, a French writer, delivereth (upon the credit of our British historians) that about this time Meroneus, a paynim king of France, caused his own son to be thrown into the fire and burned, for that he had slain the King of Cornwall, as he returned from a feast.

He also maketh mention of one Moigne, brother to Aurelius and Uter-Pendragon, Duke of Cornwall, and governor of the realm under the Emperor Honorius.

Caradoc Duke of Cornwall was employed (saith D. Kay) by Octavius, about the founding of the University of Cambridge.

And upon Igerna, wife to Gorlois Duke of Cornwall, Uter begat the worthy Arthur, and a daughter called Amy. This Arthur discomfited in fight one Childerick, a king of the Saxons, and afterwards upon certain covenants suffered him quietly to depart the realm.

But Childerick, violating the word of a king, bound with the solemnity of an oath, invaded eftsoons the western coasts, harrowing the country as he passed, until Cador Earl of Cornwall became God's minister, to take vengeance of his perjury by reaving of his life.

That Marke swayed the Cornish sceptre you cannot make question, unless you will, withal, shake the irrefragable authority of the Round Table's romance. .

Blederic Duke of Cornwall associated with other Welsh kings dar-rayned a battle against Ethelferd king of the Northumbers, and by the valiant forgoing of his life, got his partners the victory. Ivor, son to Alane king of little Britain, first won from the Saxons Cornwall, Devon and Somerset shires by force of arms, and then, taking his wife Ethelburg, cousin to Kentwin King of Wessex, enjoyed the same by composition.

Roderic, King of the Britons in Wales and Cornwall (under whom Bletius was prince of this last, and of Devon) valiantly repulsed Athelred King of Wessex, what time he assailed him in Cornwall, yet in the end being over-matched in number, and tired with continual onsets, he was driven to quit the same and retire himself into Wales.

Polydore Virgil maketh mention of one Reginaldus, *comes Britannorum* [Count of the Britons], in the time of King Etheldred.

Dungarth, King of Cornwall, by mischance was drowned.

Alpsius is recorded (about this time) for Duke of Devon and Cornwall.

Orgerius Duke of Cornwall had a daughter named Alfride, the fame of whose beauty caused King Edgar to send Earl Athelwold for obtaining her hand in marriage. But the Earl with the first sight of this fair lady was so besotted in her love that, preferring the accomplishment of his lust before the duty of his allegiance, he returns answer to the king how the common report far exceeded her private worth, which came much short of meriting a partnership in so great a prince's bed: and, not long after, begged and obtained the king's good will to wed her himself. But so brave a lustre could not lie long concealed without shining forth into Edgar's knowledge, who finding the truth of his ambassador's falsehood, took Athelwold at an advantage, slew him, and married her, being a widow, whom he had wooed a maid.

Hitherto these titles of honour carry a kind of confusedness, and rather betokened a successive office than an established dignity.

The following ages received a more distinct form and left us a certainer notice.

What time William the Bastard subdued this realm, one Condor possessed the earldom of Cornwall, and did homage for the same: he had issue another Condor, whose daughter and heir Agnes was married to Reignald Earl of Bristol, base son to King Henry I. This note I borrowed out of an industrious collection which setteth down all the notable men's creations, arms and principal descents, in every king's days since the conquest: but Master Camden, our Clarentieulx, nameth him Cadoc, and saith farther, that Robert Morton, brother to William the Conqueror by his mother Herlot, was the first Earl of Norman blood, and that his son William succeeded him; who taking part with Duke Robert against Henry I, thereby got captivity and lost his honour, with which that king invested the forementioned Reignald. In this variance it is great reason that the balance panche [inclines] on his side, who hath both authority to establish his assertion, and a rarely approved knowledge, to warrant his authority. He dying issueless, Richard I gave this earldom to his brother John.

John's son Henry III honoured therewith Richard King of the Romans, a prince no less plentifully flowing in wealth than his brother was often driven to extreme shifts, through neediness, which made that barbarous age to poetize

Nummus ait pro me, nubit Cornubia Romae.

Money said, that for her sake
Rome did Cornwall to wife take.

He had issue Henry Earl of Cornwall, who deceased issueless; and Edmond, whose daughter and heir Isabel (faith mine author) was married to Morice Fitsharding Lord Barckleigh, but others affirm that this Edmond died without issue.

Edward II, degenerating his choice, created his minion Peter Gaveston, a Gascon, Earl of this county, whose posterity ended in himself, and himself in a violent death.

The last title of this earldom expired in John of Eltham, younger son to that King Edward. After which, King Edward the Third, by Act of Parliament in the eleventh year of his reign, erected the same to a Duchy, the first in England, and graced it with his son, the Black Prince, for his heroical virtues did rather bestow than receive estimation from whatsoever dignity. Since which it is successively incorporated in the king's eldest son, and hath been so enjoyed by Richard II, Henry V, Henry VI, Edward his son, Edward V, Edward son to Richard III, Arthur and Henry, sons to Henry VII, and lastly, Edward VI, ten Dukes in the whole.

These Earls and Dukes have from the beginning been privileged with royal jurisdiction or crown rights, namely, giving of liberty to send burgesses to the parliaments, return of writs, custom, toll, mines, treasure-trove, wards, &c. and (to this end) appointed their special officers, as sheriff, Admiral, Receiver, Havener, Customer, Butler, Searcher, Comptroller, Gauger, Escheator, Feodary, Auditor, Clerk of the Market, &c, besides the Lord Warden and those others beforemembered, whose functions appertain to the jurisdiction of the Stannary.

To the preservation of which royalties our Parliaments have ever carried a reverend regard. For by the Act 17 Edw. IV which enjoineth foreign merchants to bestow such money as they receive for their wares in English commodities, or to pay the same unto Englishmen, the king's part of all forfeitures within Cornwall is reserved to the Duke. So doth 11 Henry VII, concerning the reformation of weights and measures provide that it shall not be hurtful or prejudicial to the Prince, within the Duchy of Cornwall, nor to any weights of the coinage: and so doth that 1 Henry VIII touching Escheators, exempt that officer in Cornwall. It should seem that the first Earls bare a heavy hand in command over their subjects, for both divers ancient records (as I have learned) make mention of tributes imposed (almost) upon everything of profit; and it may farther be gathered, in that, as well towns as particular persons were fain to procure charters and grants from them, for corporations, fairs, markets, taking or freeing from tolls, mines, fishing, fowling, hawking, hunting, and what not: so as (upon the matter) the plight of a Cornish inhabitant and a French peasant did differ very little.

Which bondage, one not long ago sought in part to re-establish, under pretence of reviving a rent decayed ever since the ninth of Henry II and advancing her Majesty's profit; and to this end procured letters patent that none should salt, dry, or pack any fish in Devon or Cornwall without his licence and warrant: a matter that would, by consequence, have made him an absolute disposer of all the western shipping and traffic, and their sea and land dependents.

Few words, but folding up a multitude of inconveniences to her Majesty and the whole commonwealth.

Wherefore the Cornish justices of the peace became humble suitors to the Lords of her Highness' Privy Council for a necessary and speedy redress herein, and through the never failing forwardness and backing of Sir Walter Ralegh, obtained a revocation. Howbeit, this ill weed, rather cut off by the ground than plucked up by the root, once, yea twice or thrice grew forth again, but yet, maugre the warmers and waterers, hath by her Majesty's gracious breath been ever parched up, and (as is hoped) will never shoot out hereafter; at least it shall still find an united resistance of earnest suit and pregnant reasons to beat it down.

The Earls had four houses, builded castle-wise for their residence, viz. Trematon, Launceston, Restormel, and Liskerd. But since the principality of Wales and this Duchy became united in one person, the larger scope and greater command of that, hath robbed this of his Lord's presence, and by consequence, the strength of these castles could not so guard them against the battery of time and neglect, but that, from fair buildings they fell into foul reparations, and from foul reparations are now sunk into utter ruin.

King Henry VIII affecting his honour of Newelin and respecting the commodities which Wallingford Castle might afford it, took this last by Act of Parliament from the Duchy and in lieu thereof annexed certain manors lying in Cornwall, fallen to the Crown through the Marquis of Exeter's attainder; which Queen Mary afterwards restored in tail to his son the Earl of Devon, and upon his issueless decease received them again. It were against duty to make question whether in this exchange the king's meaning went with his pretence: and yet we find it an ordinary policy among princes to send their successors, with a kind of *libera* or *honoria legatio* [free embassy, right of travel] into the remoter quarters of their dominions as if they would shun occasions of jealousy springing from an over-near neighbourhood.

Howsoever, the same king, not long after, passed away this castle unto Christ's College in Oxford, who use it as a place of retreat when the University is visited with any contagious sickness.

I have understood that question is made amongst men of knowledge, what is become of this Duchy; some holding it altogether extinct for want of the king's issue male, some averring that it is suspended *in nubibus* [among clouds, i.e. left undecided] (as they say) *pro tempore* [temporarily] and some supposing that it continueth in full power, and that her Majesty hath only *custodiam ducatus* [custody of the Duchy] as of bishoprics, *sede vacante* [when a bishop's throne is vacant]. Once, every sheriff is summoned to enter his account in the Duchy Exchequer at Lostwithiel, and from thence, referred over to the Exchequer above.

Cornwall considered as a part of the realm, sorteth her government into two kinds: spiritual and temporal.

Touching the spiritual: in ancient times this shire had his particular bishop: and I find, how in the year 905 Forinosus the Pope sent a sharp letter to Edward the son of Alfred reproving him for suffering the West Saxons to be destitute of bishops seven years together. Whereon by the advice of his Council and Archbishop Pleymund he ordained seven bishops in one day, amongst whom Herstane was consecrated to Cornwall, and Eadwolfe to Crediton, which last had three towns in Cornwall assigned to him, to wit, Pontium, Coelling and Landwhitton, that thence he might yearly visit the people to root out (as mine authority saith) their errors. For before, as much as in them lay, they withstood the truth and obeyed not the apostolic decrees. Whereon I ground two collections: the first, that the light of the gospel took not his original shining into these parts from the Roman Bishop: the other, that the Cornish (like their cousins the Welsh) could not be soon or easily induced to acknowledge his jurisdiction.

The Bishop's see was formerly at St Petrock's in Bodmyn, but by reason the Danes burned there his church and palace, the same removed to St

Germane. After that, Lumigius, from a monk of Winchester elected Abbot of Tavistoke, and from that abbey advanced to the bishopric of Creditoune by his grace with Canutus King of the Angles, obtained an annexion of Cornwall (lately fallen void) and so made one diocese of that and Devon, as it hath ever since continued. This bishopric had divers fair houses and large revenues in Cornwall, but one Veyzy, bishop of the diocese in King Henry the Eighth's time, conjecturing (as it is conceived) that the cathedral churches should not long overlive the suppressed monasteries, made havoc of those livings beforehand, some by long leasing and some by flat selling, so as he left a poor remainder to his successors.

It oweth subjection to the Metropolitan of Canterbury and hath only one Arch-deaconry, which place is now supplied by Master Thomas Sumaster, who adorneth the gentility of his birth with the honesty of his life, and by both sorts of feeding approveth himself a liberal and commendable pastor.

Certain peculiars there are, some appertaining to the dignities of the cathedral church at Exeter, to wit, St Probus and St Peran: and some to private persons, as Burien and Temple for religious houses. I read that in the time of paganism Cunedag builded a temple in Cornwall to Apollo, but where it stood I know not. Since it made room to Christianity my (not over-curious) enquiry hath learned out these:

Priories, at: St Germaine, Bodmyn, Tywardreth

Nunneries, at St Martine

Friaries, at Launceston, Truro, Bodmyn

Colleges, at Peryn, Crantock, Buryen

Hospitals, at Helston.

Of parishes, the county hath one hundred and sixty-one, as Master Camden noteth, and as others have, about one hundred and eighty.

Doubtless, the hierarchy of our English church, if it were kept fast to his first institution, might with his far better effects close up their mouths who would thrust upon us their often varying discipline. But albeit neither our time can well brook it, nor the succeeding would long hold it, yet it shall not do much amiss to look upon the original beauty thereof, if (at least) I be able to trick the same truly out, and do not blemish it with my pencil.

At the planting of the Christian religion, monasteries and cathedral churches were likewise founded, which served for seedplots of the ministry, and sent them abroad in yearly progress, to labour the Lord's vineyard. Afterwards, about the time of our last conquest, the country was sorted by a more orderly manner into parishes, and every parish committed to a spiritual father, called their parson, who stepped into that room not by election (as some imagine) but mostly by the nomination of him that built the church, or endowed the same with some livelihood, or was lord of the soil where it stood. As for vicarages, those days knew few, for they grew up in more corrupt ages, by the religious houses' encroachments. Besides this incumbent, every parish had certain officers, as churchwardens, sidesmen, and eight men whose duty bound them to see the buildings and ornaments as appertaining to God's service decently maintained, and good order there reverently observed. And lest negligence, ignorance and partiality, might admit or foist in abuses, and corruption, an Archdeacon was appointed to take account of their doings by a yearly visitation, and they were sworn duly to make it. He and they again had their Ordinary, the Bishop, every three years to overlook their actions, and to examine, allow and admit the ministers, as they and the Bishop were semblably subject to the Metropolitan's survey every seven years, for warning the clergy, and imparting their superior's directions, the curates [in an old sense, meaning senior clergy] chose yearly their deans rural. The bishop, in his cathedral church was associated with certain prebendaries, some resident, who served as his ghostly counsel in points of his charge, and others not bound to ordinary residence, who were called to consultation upon things of greater consequence, and for matters of principal importance the Archbishop had his provincial Synod, and the whole clergy their national.

Now then, if every one thus entrusted would remember that he had a soul to save or lose by the well or ill-discharging of so weighty a function, and did accordingly from time to time bestow his requisite endeavour, what the least fault could escape the espial of so many eyes, or the righting amongst so many hands? But I have thrust my sickle over-far into another's harvest: let my mistaking be corrected and in regard of my good meaning, pardoned.

The temporal government of Cornwall shooteth out also into two branches: martial and civil.

For martial affairs, Master Camden noteth out of Johannes Sarisburiensis [John of Salisbury, died 1180] that the Cornishmen's valiancy purchased them such reputation amongst our ancestors, as they (together with those of Devon and Wiltshire) were wont to be entrusted for the subsidiary cohort, or band of supply: an honour equal to the Romans' *triarii* [the most experienced soldiers], and the sheet-anchor of the battle. With which concurreth the ancient, if not authentical testimony of Michael Cornubiensis [Michael of Cornwall, writing c.1250], who had good reason to know the same, being that countryman, and more to report it: his verses, for which I have also been beholding to Mr Camden, are these:

> – – *Rex Arturus nos primos Cornubienses*
> *Bellum facturus vocat, ut puta Caesaris enses*
> *Nobis non aliis, reliquis, dat primitus ictum*
> *Per quem pax lisque, nobis fit utrumque relictum.*
> *Quid nos deterret, si firmiter in pede stemus,*
> *Fraus ne nos superet, nihil est quod non superemus.*

[King Arthur, when he intended to make war, called on us Cornish first... What shall dismay us if we stand firm? Except for treachery, there is nothing which will overcome us.]

I will now set down the principal commanders and officers touching these martial causes, together with the forces of the shire.

Lord Lieutenant General: Sir Walter Ralegh.

Deputy Lieutenants: Sir Frauncis Godolphin, Sir Nicholas Parker, Sir Reignald Mohun, Peter Edgecumb, Bernard Greinvile, Christopher Harris, Richard Carew, or any three of them.

Colonel General: Sir Nicholas Parker.

Marshal: Bernard Greinvile.

Treasurer: Richard Carew.

Master of the Ordnance: Will. Treffry.

Colonel of the Horse: John Arundell of Trerise.

Sergeant Major: Humfrey Parcks.

Quarter Master: William Carnsew.

Provost Marshal: John Harris.

Scout Master: Otwell Hill.

Corporals of the Field: Osburne, Rusall, Rattenbury, Sled.

Ammunition Master: Leon. Blackdon.

Trench Master: Cooke.

Regiments.	Com-panies	Num-ber	Arm. pikes	Muskets	Calivers	
Sir Fra. Godol.	12	1200	470	490	240	
Sir Will. Bevil	6	670	225	315	130	
Sir Rei. Mohun	6	600	200	210	190	
Ber. Greinvile	10	1000	370	390	240	
Ri. Carew	5	500	170	300	30	For Causand Bay
Anthony Rouse	6	760	270	320	170	
Ch. Trevanion	5	500	180	190	130	
Will. Treffry	4	400	140	130	130	For Foy.
Sir Nic. Parker	2	200	60	80	60	For Pendenis.
Ha. Vivian	1	100	40	40	20	For St Mawes.
Ar. Harris	1	100	40	40	20	For the Mount.
Summa	58	6030	2165	2535	1330	

This may serve for a general estimate of the Cornish forces, which I have gathered, partly out of our certificate made to the Lords 1599, partly by information from the sergeant major, and partly through mine own knowledge. There are many more unarmed pikes, which I omit, as better fitting a supply upon necessity, than to be exposed (or opposed) to an enemy. The number as it standeth, much exceedeth the shire's proportion, if the same be compared with Devon and other counties, which groweth for that their nearness on all quarters to the enemy, and their farness from timely succour by their friends, have forced the commanders to call forth the uttermost number of able hands to fight, and rather by persuasion than authority, procured them to arm themselves beyond law and their ability. Which commendable endeavour shall not, I hope, ought not, I am sure, turn them to the prejudice of any unwonted charge hereafter. They are all provided of powder, bullet and match in competent sort, and order taken for furnishing of victuals and mounting a third part of the shot (at least) upon cause of service.

Light horses the Lords in their directions enjoin for order's sake, and the lieutenants excuse it by insufficiency. Hitherto neither hath the commandment been revoked, nor the omission controlled.

In the year 1588, when the Spanish floating Babel pretended the conquest of our island (which, like Joshua's army, they compassed, but unlike him could not with their blasting threats overthrow our walls) it pleased her Majesty, of her provident and gracious care, to furnish Cornwall with ordnance and ammunition from her own store, as followeth:

2 sacres	}	of cast iron, well mounted upon carriages with wheels, shod with iron, and furnished with ladles, sponges and rammers, with all other accessories.
2 minions		
2 faulcons		

Spare axletrees, six

Spare pairs of wheels shod with iron, three

Shot of iron for the said pieces, of each sort twenty

Cannon corn powder for the said ordnance, six hundredweight

Fine corn powder, three hundredweight

Lead, three thousand six hundredweight

Match, three thousand six hundredweight

All which, save the ordnance itself, partly by piecemeal employment, and partly by overlong and evil keeping, is now grown to nought, or naught.

After the sudden surprise of Pensants, *anno* 1595, by direction from the Lords, order was taken, that upon any alarum the next captains should forthwith put themselves with their companies into their assigned sea-coast towns, whom the adjoining land forces were appointed to second and third, as the opportunity of their dwellings afforded best occasion.

The year following, by a new command, 4000 were allotted out and provided in a readiness to march for the aid of Devon if cause so required, as the lord lieutenant of that county had the same order, upon like neces-sity, to send an equal number into Cornwall.

Lastly, *anno* 1599, when the Spanish fleet was again expected, the Cornish forces voluntarily assembled themselves, and made head at the entrance, middle, and west part of their south coast.

As for soldiers sent into other places, Cornwall yieldeth upon every occasion a proportionable supply to the wants of Ireland, neither is acquitted from performing the like service for France, if the employment be in Brittany or Normandy. Which often venturings notwithstanding, upon the influence of Captain Lower and the solicitations of his friends, there passed over this last year into Netherland at one time 100 volun-taries and others, there to serve under Sir Fruancis Vere. And besides, they often make out men of war against the Spaniard.

Forts and castles there are: some old and worn out of date, and some in present use, with allowance of garrison. Amongst the first sort I reckon these, appertaining to the Duchy, as also Tintogel, and divers round holds on the tops of hills, some single, some double and treble trenched, which are termed *Castellan denis*, or *Danis*, as raised by the Danes, when they were destined to became our scourge.

Moreover in this rank we may muster the earthen bulwarks cast up in divers places on the south coast, where any commodity of landing seemeth to invite the enemy, which (I guess) took their original from the statute 4 Henry VIII, and are ever since duly repaired, as need requireth, by order to the captains of those limits.

Of the latter sort there is a fort at Scilley, called [gap in text: actually Star Castle] reduced to a more defensible plight by her Majesty's order, and governed by the foreremembered Sir Frauncis Godolphin, who with his invention and purse bettered his plot and allowance, and therein hath so tempered strength with delight, and both with use, as it serveth for a sure hold and a commodious dwelling.

The rest are St Michael's Mount, Pendenis Fort, and St Mawes Castle, of which I shall have occasion to speak more particularly in my second book.

Of beacons, through the nearness to the sea, and the advantage of the hilly situations, wellnear every parish is charged with one, which are watched *secundum usum* [according to custom], but (so far as I can see) not greatly *ad propositum* [relevantly]: for the Lords' better digested instructions have reduced the country, by other means, to a like ready and much less confused way of assembling upon any cause of service. For carrying of such advertisements and letters, every thoroughfare weekly appointeth a foot-post to give his hourly attendance, whose dispatch is wellnear as speedy as the horse's.

The last branch of my division, and so of this book, leadeth me to entreat of Cornwall's civil government, as it passeth for a part of the realm; and that may again be subdivided into jurisdiction particular and general. The particular jurisdiction is exercised by constables, stewards of courts barons and leets, franchises, hundreds, and portreeves and mayors; of boroughs and corporations of the stannaries we have already spoken. The general, by the clerk of the market, coroners, vice-admiral, sheriff, justices of the peace, and judges of assize.

Constables of the hundreds the shire hath none, but this office for giving of warnings and collection of rates is supplied by the deputy bailiffs, who perform it not with that discretion, trust, secrecy, and speed which were often requisite to the importance of the affairs. I have known the judges moved divers times for their opinion touching the erecting of some, and found them of several resolutions, which giveth little encouragement to an innovation. Neither can the parish constables well brook the same, because it submitteth them to a subaltern command, more than of custom; whereas now in their parishes they are absolute, the least whereof hath one, the middle sized two, the bigger three or four. I would not wish the blaze of their authority blemished, if there were as much care used in choice of the persons as the credit of their place deserveth. Wise direction without diligent execution proveth fruitless. Now, as the former is derived from her Majesty to the Lords, and from the Lords to the justices, so this latter lieth in the hands of the constables. Watches and searches often carry weighty consequence, and miscarry in the managing: and it was seen in the last Cornish rebellion, how the constables' command and example drew many of the not worst meaning people into that extremest breach of duties.

Franchises, Cornwall hath the Duchy, Rialton, Clifton, Minhinet, Pawton, Carnanton, Stoke Climsland, Medland and Kellylond, which have their bailiffs as the hundreds, to attend the public services.

Hundreds there are but nine: East, West, Trig, Lesnewith, Stratton, Powder, Pider, Kerier, and Penwith, which contain [gap in text] tithings: by these the shire is divided into limits, and all his rates proportioned as followeth:

Divisions

East	East H., West H.
North	Trig H., Lesnewith H., Stratton H.
South	Powder H., Pider H.
West	Kerier H. Penwith H.

In all rates, the East and South limits bear three parts in five, to the North and West. So in the eastern, doth the East Hundred to that of West: in the Southern, Powder to Pider; and in the western, Kerier to Penwith. In the northern, Trig beareth five, Lesnewith and Stratton four apiece. There is the like proportion made of the parishes in the eastern division, but with little satisfaction of divers: neither will it ever fare otherwise, and therefore (this notwithstanding) I wish it followed in the residue.

The convenientest and usual places of assembly for the whole county is at Bodmyn; for the East and North, Launceston; for the South and West, Truro; for the East, Liskerd; for the North, Camelford; for the South, St Columbs; for the West, Helston. For the Hundreds of East, Kellington; of West, Lanreath; of Trig, Bodmyn; of Lesnewith, Camelford; of Stratton, that town; of Powder, Grampond; of Pider, St Columbs; of Kerier, Helston; of Penwith, Pensants.

Corporations are privileged with the administration of justice within their liberties, more or less, according to the purport of their charter. Such are Saltash, Launceston, Liskerd, East Loo, West Loo, Bodmyn, Camelford, Lostwithiel, Padstowe, Grampond, Truro, Helston, Perin.

The mayors and recorders in some of these are justices of the peace for their own limits, and wellnear all of them have large exemptions and jurisdictions, a garment (in divers men's opinions) over-rich and wide for many of their wearish and ill-disposed bodies. They allege for themselves that speedy justice is administered in their towns, and that it saveth great expenses incident to assize trials, which poor artificers cannot undergo. But the other answer that these trials are often posted on with more haste than good speed, while an ignorant fellow of a souter [cobbler] becomes a magistrate, and takes upon him peremptory judgment in debts and controversies great and doubtful. Again, the nearness of commencing their suits draweth on more expenses than the shortness of trials cutteth off, whereas longer respite would make way to deliberation, and deliberation open the door to reason, which by the fumes arising from choler's boiling heat, is much obscured. Thus doth the opportunity inure them to vexation; vexation begetteth charges, and charge hatcheth poverty: which poverty, accompanied with idleness (for they cannot follow law, and work) seeketh not to relieve itself by industry, but by subtlety, wherethrough they become altogether depraved in body, goods, and mind. Add hereunto, that the mayor exercising his office but during one year, for the first half thereof is commonly to learn what he ought to do, and in the other half, feeling his authority to wane, maketh friends of that mammon, and serveth others' turns to be requited with the like, borrowing from justice what he may lend to his purse or complices: for as it hath been well said, 'He cannot long be good, that knows not why he is good.' They conclude, how from these imperfect associations there spring pride amongst themselves, disdain at their neighbours, and monopolies against the commonwealth.

This invective is somewhat deeply steeped in gall, and must therefore be interpreted, not of all, but the worst. Surely, for mine own part, I am of opinion that how commodious soever this jurisdiction may prove amongst themselves, it falleth out sundry times very distasteful and injurious towards strangers, and strangers they reckon all that are not burgesses. Now, let such a one be arrested within their corporations, no sureties but townsmen can find acceptance, be his behaviour never so honest, his cause never so just, his calling never so regardful, and his ability never so sufficient; yet, if he have none acquaintance in the town, if the action brought carry a show of weight, if the bringer be a man of sway in or near the town, if any other townsman of the higher sort bear him an old grudge, he must be contented to fret the cold irons with his legs, and his heart with grief; for what one amongst them will procure an everlasting enemy at his door, by becoming surety for a party in whom he possesseth none, or little interest?

The ancients used to grace their cities with several titles, as *Numantia bellicosa, Thebae superbae, Corinthus ornata, Athena docta, Hierusalem sancta, Carthago emula*, &c [Proud Thebes, Learned Athens, etc], and the present Italians do the like touching theirs, as *Roma Santa, Venezia ricca, Firenze bella, Napoli gentile, Ravenna antiqua*, &c. In an imitation whereof, some of the idle disposed Cornishmen nick their towns with by-words, as, The Good Fellowship of Padstowe, Pride of Truro, Gallants of Foy, &c.

The Clerk of the Market's office hath been heretofore so abused by his deputies, to their private gain, that the same is tainted with a kind of discredit, which notwithstanding, being rightly and duly executed would work reformation of many disorders, and a great good to the Commonwealth.

Four Coroners, chosen by the voices of the free-holders, do serve the shire, who for the present are Bligh, Tub, Trenance and Bastard.

The vice-admiralty is exercised by Mr Charles Trevanion, a gentleman through his virtue as free from greediness, as through his fair livelihood far from neediness; and by daily experience giving proof, that a mind valuing his reputation at the due price, will easily repute all dishonest gain much inferior thereunto, and that in conversing with the worst sort of people (which his office oftentimes enforceth) he can no more be disgraced than the sunbeams by shining upon a dunghill will be blemished.

I have here set down the names of those commissioners for the peace, who at this present make their ordinary residence in Cornwall, as they stand placed in the commission, where the priority is mostly deferred to antiquity.

Q.	Fra. Godolphin M.	1.		Carolus Trevanion	16.
Q.	Nic. Parker M.	2.		Thomas St Aubin	17.
Q.	Jona. Trelawney M.	3.	Q.	Rob. Moyle	18.
Q.	Reg. Mohun M.	4.	Q.	Ed. Hancock	19.
Q.	P. Petrus Edgecomb	5.		Tristramus Arscot	20.
Q.	Ric. Carew de Anth.	6.		Thomas Lower	21.
Q.	Bern. Greinvile	7.		W. Treffry de Fowey	22.
Q.	Antonius Rowse	8.		Johannes Henser	23.
	Petrus Courtney	9.	Q.	Willi. Wray	24.
Q.	Tho. Chiverton	10.		Georgius Kekiwiche	25.
Q.	Christ. Harris	11.	Q.	Arth. Harris	26.
	Jo. Arund. de Trerise	12.		Jo. Harris de Lansre.	27.
	T. Arun. de Talverne	13.	Q.	Degor. Chamons	28.
Q.	Nic. Prideaux	14.		Johannes Trefusis	29.
Q.	Hannibal Vivian	15.		Otwel Hill	30.

Their ordinary use was to begin the quarter sessions for the east half of the shire on the Tuesdays and Wednesdays at Bodmyn, and to adjourn the same for the west half to be ended at Truro the Friday and Saturday following, leaving one day's space for riding between. But about twenty years sithence, the eastern justices making the greatest number, and in this separation having farthest to ride when they were disposed to attend both places, either in regard of their ease or upon scruple of conscience or for both together, called into question whether this custom were as warrantable by right as it was pleadable by prescription, and whether it as much advanced the administration of justice as it eased the travel of the people. And thereupon they began to appoint the entire sessions at either place one after another. This was sometimes performed and sometimes broken by the western justices, so as several contrary precepts of summons were directed to the sheriff, with the great uncertainty, ill example, and trouble of the country. It happened, that one newly associated, and not yet seasoned with either humour, made this motion for a reconcilement, viz. that the sessions should interchangeably one quarter begin at Bodmyn and end at Truro, and the next begin at Truro and end at Bodmyn, and that no recognizance should be discharged or cause decided out of his own division. This proposition, as it gave the western justices the greatest part of their will, so it salved a sore which chiefly grieved the eastern; for before, what was done in the beginning at one place was, or might be, undone in the ending at the other; wherefore all parties willingly condescended hereunto, and it hath ever sithence been accordingly observed.

Another variance hath sometimes fallen out between Devon and Cornwall, about the time of keeping their sessions. For whereas Statute 2 Henry V enacteth that the justices shall hold the same in the first week after St Michael, the Epiphany, the clause [conclusion] of Easter, and the translation of St Thomas (which, worthily blotted out of the Calendar, *teste Newbrigensi* [according to Newbridge] is ever the seventh of July) and their oath bindeth them to a strict observation hereof; the question hath grown, when those festival days fall upon a Monday, whether the Sessions shall be proclaimed for that week, or the next, and the general practice hath gone with the former.

But the Cornish justices, weighing that prescription is no *supersedeas* for [bar to] swearing, upon debating of the matter have resolved, and lately accustomed, in such cases to put it over to the week ensuing: and these are their reasons: if the Sessions must be kept in the full week after, it cannot admit an interpretation of the same week itself. Again, the clause of Easter, mentioned in the one, should seem to make a construction of like meaning in the rest. Besides, those who suit themselves to the other fashion do yet swerve therefrom if those feasts fall upon any later day in the week than Monday, for then they defer it to the next. And yet, seeing no day certain is directed for beginning the Sessions, if they will constantly bind themselves to the former sense, when those days fall on the Friday, they ought to call it for the morrow following. The judges of the Circuit's Oracle, to which the Commission of the peace referreth the justices' *Quaeres* [enquiries], hath resolved that neither of these ways tendeth to any breach of the law. Once sure it is, that the term-suiters may best speed their business by supporting the former: for the end of these Sessions delivereth them space enough to overtake the beginning of the terms.

For the rest, equity beareth more sway than gravity at the Cornish bench, and in confusion they maintain equality; for though they speak more than one at once, yet no man's speech or countenance can carry a matter against the truth. Neither do assertions but proofs, in hearings, nor vouchings but showing of law cases, in deciding, order the controversies; and as diversity in opinions breedeth no enmity, so overruling by most voices is taken for no disgrace.

One only judge was wont, in three days at farthest, to dispatch the assizes and gaol delivery at Launceston, the usual (though not indifferentest) place where they are holden. But malice and iniquity have so increased, through two contrary effects, wealth and poverty, that now necessity exacteth the presence of both, and (not seldom) an extent of time.

I have heard the judges note, that besides their ordinary pains they are troubled with more extraordinary supplications in Cornwall than in any other shire; whereto they yet give no great encouragement, while the causes are on the backside, posted over to Gentlemen's hearing, and account seldom taken or made what hath been done therein.

Verily, we must acknowledge, that ever since our remembrance, God hath blessed this western circuit with special choice of upright and honest judges, amongst whom this of our last is not the least; for they do so temper a quick conceit with a staid judgment, a strict severity in punishing with a mild mercy in remitting, and an awful gravity at the bench with a familiar kindness in conversation, as they make proof that contrary virtues may, by the divers ways of love and reverence, meet in one only point of honour.

The common gaol of the shire for offenders is kept at Launceston: for that statute, 33 Henry VIII, which amongst other shires gave Cornish justices leave to alter the same, by a Proviso, took it away again, in that this keepership is annexed to the Constableship of the castle, and that granted out in lease.

I will conclude with the highest jurisdiction, namely the Parliament, to which Cornwall, through the grace of his Earls sendeth an equal, if not larger number of burgesses, to any other shire. The boroughs so privileged, more of favour (as the case now standeth with many of them) than merit, are these following: Launceston, Downevet [Dunheved – a part of Launceston], Liskerd, Lostwithiel, Truro, Bodmyn, Helston, Saltash, Camelford, East Loo, West Loo, Prury [Penryn], Tregny, Kellington, Bossiney, St Ives, St Germanes, Meddishole [Mitchell], and St Mawes; and because *quindec.* [taxes of one fifteenth part] are ordinarily granted at Parliaments, together with the subsidies, I will here set down the ordinary rate of them. [This table has been omitted.]

The Second Book

In this second book I will first report what I have learned of Cornwall and Cornishmen in general, and from thence descend to the particular places and persons, as their noteworthy site, or any memorable action or accident of the former or later ages shall offer occasion.

The highest which my search can reach unto I borrow out of Strabo, who writeth that the western Britons gave aid unto the Armorici of France against Caesar, which he pretended for one of the causes why he invaded this island.

Next I find, that about sixty years from the landing of Hengist, one Nazaleod, a mighty king amongst the Britons, joined battle with Certicus, sovereign of the West Saxons, and after long fight, with his own death accomplished the overthrow of his army. Yet the Britons, thus abandoned by fortune, would not so forsake themselves, but with renewed courage and forces coped once again with Certicus, and his son Kenrick, at Certicesford, though equally destitute of success as before.

Gurmund, an arch pirate of the Norwegians, was called by the Saxons out of his late conquered Ireland, to their aid, against Careticus king of the Britons, whom he overcame in battle, and enforced his subjects to seek safety by flight, some in Wales, some in Cornwall, and some in little Britain [Brittany]: since which time, they could never recover again their ancient possession of the whole island.

Howbeit, not long after, Ivor, son to Alane king of the said little Britain, landed in the west parts, won from the Saxons Cornwall, Devon and Somerset shires, by force of arms, and then established his conquest by a peaceable composition with his adverse party.

Adelred king of Wessex invaded Devon and Cornwall, whom Roderick, king of the Britons, and Blederick, prince of those provinces, encountered and discomfited. Which notwithstanding, process of time reaved from him and added such strength to his enemies that he was driven to abandon Cornwall and retire into Wales.

So, the Cornishmen quitted their liberty with their prince, stooped to the command of Egbert king of Wessex, and with their territory (says William of Malmesbury) enlarged his confines.

Athelstane handled them yet more extremely; for he drave them out of

Excester, where, till then, they bare equal sway with the Saxons, and left only the narrow angle on the west of Tamer River for their inhabitancy, which hath ever since been their fatal bound.

On their *Reguli* [petty kings] (as Vincentius delivereth) he imposed a yearly tribute of £20 in gold, £300 in silver, 25 oxen, and hunting hounds and hawks at discretion.

To these afflictions of home-neighbours of bondage, tribute, and banishing was joined a fourth, of spoiling by foreign enemies; for Roger Hovedon telleth us that the Danes landed in sundry places of Cornwall, forayed the country, burned the towns, and killed the people.

To whom succeeded in the like occupation Godwin and Edmund Magnus, King Harold's two sons, discomfiting the forces opposed against them, harrowing Devon and Cornwall and then retiring with their prey into Ireland.

After the conquest, when King Henry I invaded Griffin ap Conan Prince of Wales, he distributed his army into three portions, one of which (wherein consisted the fourth part of England and Cornwall) he committed to the leading of Gilbert Earl of Strigill.

In Henry III's time, by the testimony of Matthew Paris, William Earl of Sarum after long tossing at sea, with much ado, about Christmas arrived in Cornwall; and so afterwards did Earl Richard, the King's brother, at two several times: the latter of which, being destitute of horses and treasure, he prayed therein aid of his loyals.

When Edward III averred his right to the Crown of France, by the evidence of arms, the French for a counterplea made an unlawful entry into Devon and Cornwall; but Hugh Courtney Earl of Devon removed it with a *posse comitatus* [literally the power of the County, a 'posse' raised by the sheriff], and recommitted them to the wooden prison that brought them thither. Yet would not the Scots take so much warning by their success, as example by their precedent, if at least Froissart's ignorance of our English names bred not his mistaking in the place.

By his relation also, Cornwall's near neighbourhood gave opportunity of access, both to the Earl Montfort when he appealed to that king's aid, for recovering his right in Britain (albeit I cannot bring home 'Cepsee', the designed port of his landing) and after his captivity, to the messengers of his heroical countess, employed in the like errand.

And from Cornwall, the Earl of Sarum, William de Mesvile and Philip de Courtney set to sea with 40 ships, besides barks, and 2000 men at arms, besides archers, in support of that quarrel.

Lastly his authority informeth me that those soldiers of Cornwall who under their captains, John Apport and John Cornwall, had defended the Fort of Bercherel in Brittany against the power of France above a year's space, in the end for want of due succours, upon an honourable composition, surrendered the same.

Queen Margaret, wife to Henry VI, upon her arrival out of France after the loss of Barnet field, 1471, received great aid, though to small purpose, from the Devon and Cornish men, under the conduct of Thomas [Courtenay], Earl of that shire. And so much were those western people addicted to that name, as they readily followed Sir Edward Courtney and his brother Peter, Bishop of Excester, what time they assisted the Duke of Buckingham in his revolt against Richard III, in 1485.

Neither did his suppressor and successor, Henry VII, find them more loyal; for the Cornishmen, repining at a subsidy lately granted him by Act of Parliament, were induced to rebellion by Thomas Flammock, a gentleman, and Michael Joseph, a blacksmith, with whom they marched to Taunton, there murdering the Provost of Perin, a commissioner for the said subsidy, and from thence to Wells, where James Touchet, Lord Audley, degenerated to their party, with which increase they passed by Salisbury to Winchester, and so into Kent. But by this time Lords and Commons were gathered in strength sufficient to make head against them, and soon after, Blackheath saw the overthrow of their forces in battle, and London the punishment of their seducers by justice.

In the same fatal year of revolts, Perkin Warbeck, a counterfeit prince, landed in Cornwall, went to Bodmin, assembled a train of rake-hells, assaulted Exeter, received the repulse, and in the end sped as is known, and as he deserved.

The last Cornish rebellion was first occasioned by one Kilter and other his associates of a western parish called St Keveren, who imbrued their wicked hands in the guiltless blood of one Mr Body, as he sat in commission at Helston for matters of reformation in religion: and the year following it grew to a general revolt under Arundel, Wydeslade, Resogan, and others, followed by 6000, with which power they marched into Devon, besieged and assaulted Excester, and gave the Lord Russell (employed with an army against them) more than one hot encounter, which yet (as ever) quailed in their overthrow.

In my particular view, I will make easy journeys from place to place, as they lie in my way, taking the hundreds for my guides, until I have accomplished this wearisome voyage.

My first entrance must be by the hundred of East, so named for his site, and therein at Plymmouth haven. It borroweth that name of the river Plym, which rising in Devon, and by the way baptizing Plymston, Plymstock, &c. here emptieth itself into the sea. The haven parteth Devon and Cornwall wellnear every where as Tamer river runneth: I say wellnear, because some few interlaced places are excepted, a matter so sorted at the first partition, either to satisfy the affection of some special persons, or to appropriate the soil to the former lords, or that (notwithstanding this severance) there might still rest some cause of intercourse between the inhabitants of both counties, as I have heard a late great man ensued and expressed the like consideration in division of his lands between two of his sons.

Now though this haven thus bound both shires, yet doth the jurisdiction of the water wholly appertain to the Duchy of Cornwall, and may therefore be claimed as a part of that county. Notwithstanding, I will forbear what I may, to intrude upon my good friend Mr Hooker's limits, and reserve to him the description of the farther shore.

The first promontory of this harbour on the west side is Rame Head, by his proportion receiving, and by his possession giving, that name and arms to his owner, whose posterity conveyed it by intermarriages from Durnford to Edgecumb. On the top thereof riseth a little vaulted chapel, which serveth for a mark at sea.

From thence trending Penlee Point, you discover King's sand and Cawsam Bay, an open road, yet sometimes affording succour to the worst sort of seafarers, as not subject to controlment of Plymmouth forts. The shore is peopled with some dwelling houses, and many cellars, dearly rented for a short usage in saving of pilchard. At which time there flocketh a great concourse of seiners, and others depending upon their labour. I have heard the inhabitants thereabouts to report that the Earl of Richmond (afterwards Henry the Seventh), while he hovered upon the coast, here by stealth refreshed himself, but being advertised of strait watch kept for his surprising at Plymmouth, he richly rewarded his host, hied speedily a shipboard, and escaped happily to a better fortune.

Here also of late years, part of the Cornish forces twice encamped themselves, planted some ordnance, and raised a weak kind of fortification, therethrough to contest, if not repulse, the landing of the expected enemy: and a strong watch is continually kept there ever since 1597, at which time, a Spaniard riding on the bay while most of the able people gave their attendance at the county Assizes, sent some closely into the village in the dark of night, who hanged up barrels of matter fit to take fire upon certain doors, which by a train should have burned the houses. But one of the inhabitants espying these unwelcome guests, with the bounce of a caliver chased them aboard, and removed the barrels before the trains came to work their effect. The engineer of this practice (as hath since appeared by some examinations) was a Portugal [Portuguese], who sometimes sailed with Sir John Borowghs, and boasted to have burned his ship: for which two honourable exploits, the King of Spain bestowed on him 200 ducats.

In the mouth of the harbour lieth St Nicholas Island, in fashion lozengy, in quantity about three acres, strongly fortified, carefully guarded, and subject to the commander of Plymmouth fort. When the Cornish rebels, during Edward VI's reign, turmoiled the quiet of those quarters, it yielded a safe protection to divers dutiful subjects who there shrouded themselves.

From this island a range of rocks reacheth over to the south-west shore, discovered at the low water of spring tides and leaving only a narrow entrance in the midst, called the Yate, for ships to pass through, whereto they are directed by certain marks at land.

Upon this south shore, somewhat within the island, standeth Mount Edgecumb, a house builded and named by Sir Richard Edgecumb, father to the now possessioner: and if comparisons were as lawful in the making as they prove odious in the matching, I would presume to rank it, for health, leisure, and commodities, with any subject's house of his degree in England. It is seated against the north, on the declining of a hill in the midst of a deer park, near a narrow entrance through which the salt water breaketh up into the country to shape the greatest part of the haven. The house is builded square, with a round turret at each end, garretted on the top, and the hall rising in the midst above the rest, which yieldeth a stately sound as you enter the same. In summer, the opened casements admit a refreshing coolness, in winter, the two closed doors exclude all offensive coldness; the parlour and dining chamber give you a large and diversified prospect of land and sea, to which underlie St Nicholas Island, Plymmouth fort, and the towns of Plymmouth, Stonehouse, Milbrook, and Saltash. It is supplied with a never-failing spring of water, and the dwelling stored with wood, timber, fruit, deer, and conies. The ground abundantly answereth a housekeeper's necessities, for pasture, arable, and meadow, and is replenished with a kind of stone serving both for building, lime, and marl. On the sea cliffs groweth great plenty of the best ore-wood, to satisfy the owner's want and accommodate his neighbours. A little below the house, in the summer evenings, sein-boats come and draw with their nets for fish, whither the gentry of the house walking down, take the pleasure of the sight, and sometimes, at all adventures, buy the profit of the draughts.

Both sides of the forementioned narrow entrance, together with the passage between (much haunted as the highway to Plymmouth), the whole town of Stonehouse, and a great circuit of the land adjoining) appertain to Mr Edgecumb's inheritance. These sides are fenced with blockhouses, and that next to Mount Edgecumb was wont to be planted with ordnance which, at coming and parting, with their bass voices greeted such guests as visited the house; neither hath the opportunity of the harbour wanted occasions to bring them, or the owners a frank mind to invite them. For proof whereof, the erst remembered Sir Richard (a gentleman in whom mildness and stoutness, diffidence and wisdom, deliberateness of undertaking and sufficiency of effecting, made a more commendable than blazing mixture of virtue) during Queen Mary's reign, entertained at one time, for some good space, the Admirals of the English, Spanish, and Netherland fleets, with many noble men besides. But not too much of this, lest a partial affection steal at unwares into my commendation, as one by my mother descended from his loins, and by my birth a member of the house.

Certain old ruins yet remaining, confirm the neighbours' report that near the water's side there stood once a town called West stone house, until the French by fire and sword overthrew it.

In the year 1599 the Spaniards' vaunts caused the Cornish forces to advance there a kind of fortification, and to plot the making of a bridge on barges over that strait, for inhibiting the enemy's access by boats and galleys into the inward parts of the haven. But it may be doubted whether the bridge would have proved as impossible as the sconce fell out unnecessary.

Master Peter Edgecumbe (commonly called Piers) married Margaret, the daughter of Sir Andrew Lutterel, his father Sir Richard married [gap in text] the daughter of Tregian: his father Sir Peers married [gap in text] the daughter and heir of Stephen Durnford: and his father Sir Richard married [gap in text] the daughter of Tremayn. These names of Peers and Richard they have successively varied for six or seven descents. He beareth for his arms Gules on a Bend Ermine, between two Cotises, Or, three boars' heads coped, arg, armed as the three; langued is the field.

A little inward from Mount Edgecumb lieth a safe and commodious road for shipping, called Hamose, and compounded of the words ose [ooze] and ham, according to the nature of the place. Here those vessels cast anchor which are bound to the eastward, as those do in Catwater, who would fare to the west, because every wind that can serve them at sea will from thence carry them out, which commodity other roads do not so conveniently afford. It is reported that in times past there was an ordinary passage over this water to a place on the Devon side called Horsecove, but long since discontinued.

At the higher end of a creek, passing up from hence, Milbrook lurketh between two hills, a village of some eighty houses, and borrowing its name from a mill and little brook running therethrough. In my remembrance (which extendeth not to above forty years) this village took great increase of wealth and buildings through the just and industrious trade of fishing, and had wellnear forty ships and barks at one time belonging thereunto; but our late broils with Spain have set up a more compendious, though not so honest way of gaining, and begin by little and little to reduce these plain dealers to their former undeserved plight. Yet do they prescribe, in a suburbial market (as I may term it) to Plymmouth for their relief, by intercepting, if not forestalling, such corn and victuals as passing through their straits cannot, for want of time or weather, get over Crymell passage to the other; and surely they are not unworthy of favour, for this town furnisheth more able mariners at every prest for her Highness's service than many others of far greater blaze.

It chanced about twenty years sithence that one Richaurd, wife to Richard Adams of this town, was delivered of two male children, the one ten weeks after the other, who lived until baptism, and the latter hitherto;

which might happen, in that the woman, bearing twins, by some blow, slide, or other extraordinary accident, brought forth the first before his time, and the later in his due season. Now, that a child born in the seventh month may live, both astrologers and physicians do affirm, but in the eighth they deny it, and these are their reasons: the astrologers hold that the child in the mother's womb is successively governed every month by the seven planets, beginning at Saturn, after which reckoning, he returning to his rule the eighth month, by his dreary influence infortunateth any birth that shall then casually befall: whereas his succeeder, Jupiter, by a better disposition, worketh a more beneficial effect. The physicians deliver that in the seventh month the child, by course of nature, turneth itself in the mother's belly, wherefore at that time it is readier (as half loosed) to take issue by any outward chance; marry, in the eighth, when it beginneth to settle again, and as yet retaineth some weakness of the former stirring, it requireth a more forcible occasion, and that induceth a slaughtering violence. Or if these conjectural reasons suffice not to warrant a probability of the truth, Pliny's authority in a stranger case shall press them farther, for he writeth that a woman brought to bed of one child in the seventh month, in the months following was also delivered of twins.

A part of Mount-Edgecumb, and of this Milbrook, though severed from Devon by the general bound, yet upon some of the foreremembered considerations have been annexed thereunto.

Aside of Milbrook lieth the peninsula of Inswork, on whose neckland standeth an ancient house of the Champernons, and descended by his daughters and heirs to Forteskew, Monck and Trevilian, three gentlemen of Devon. The site is naturally both pleasant and profitable; to which the owner by his ingenious experiments daily addeth an artificial surplusage.

Passing somewhat farther up you meet with the foot of Lyner where it winneth fellowship with Tamer, that till then, and this yet longer, retaining their names, though their over-weak streams were long before confounded by the predominant salt water. A little within this mouth of Lyner standeth East-Antony, the poor home of mine ancestors, with which in this manner they were invested.

Sir John Lerchedekne [l'Archdeacon], knight, and not priest (for he was so called of his family, and not by his calling, as in Froissart you shall note the like to be familiar amongst the nobility of Gascony), by Cecill [Cecilia], the daughter and heir of Jordan of Haccumb, had issue nine sons, Ralph, Waryne, Richard, Otho, John, Robert, Martyn, Reignald and Michael. Richard married Jone, the daughter of John Bosowr, that bare him Thomas in whom the heirs male of this multiplied hope took an end. Warine, afterwards knighted, took to wife Elizabeth, one of the daughters and heiress to John Talbot de Castro Ricardi, and on her begat three daughters and heirs: Alienor, wedded to Sir Walter Lucy; Margery to Sir Thomas Arundel of Talverne; and Philip[pa] to Sir Hugh Courtney of Baunction (which I take is now named Boconnock). From Lucy descended the Lord Vaux, and others. Margery died childless, *anno* 1419, as is testified by her tombstone in West-Antony church, where she lieth buried. Sir Hugh Courtney was second son to Ed. Earl of Devon, and had two wives: the first, Maud, daughter of the Lord Beaumond, to whose children, for want of issue in the elder stock that Earldom devolved, and the later, our foreremembered Philip[pa], who left her inheritance to her only daughter Jone; and she, taking a pattern from her father's fortune, espoused likewise two husbands, viz. Sir Nicholas, Baron of Carew, and Sir Robert Vere, brother to John Earl of Oxford. To Sir Nicholas she bare Thomas, Nicholas, Hugh, Alexander, and William; to Sir Robert, John, and became widow of both.

And as, after the father's decease, good agreement between the mother and eldest son hath commonly weak continuance, because both being enfranchised to a sudden absolute jurisdiction, neither of them can easily temper the same with a requisite moderation, so it chanced that she and hers fell at square, which discord (with an unnatural extremity) brake forth into a blow, by him no less dearly than undutifully given his mother; for upon so just a cause she disinherited him of all her lands, being seventeen manors, and bestowed them on her younger sons. This I learned by the report of Sir Peter Carew, the elder of that name, and eldest of our stock (a gentleman whose rare worth my pen is not able to shadow, much less with his due lineaments to represent) at such time, as being a scholar in Oxford of fourteen years of age, and three years standing, upon a wrong conceived opinion touching my sufficiency, I was there called to dispute *ex tempore (impar congressus Achilli* [no match for Achilles]) with the matchless Sir Philip Sidney, in presence of the Earls Leicester, Warwick, and divers other great personages.

By the forementioned conveyance, she disposed of her said manors as followeth: Haccumb, Ringmore and Milton she gave to Nicholas, Lyham,

Manedon, Combhall and South Tawton to Hugh: East-Antony, Shogge-broke and Landegy to Alexander: Wicheband, Widebridge, Bokeland and Bledeuagh to William: and lastly Roseworthy, Bosewen and Tregennow to John: all which she entailed to them, and the issue of their bodies, substi-tuting, for want thereof, the one to be heir to the other and in witness hereof (saith she in her conveyance) to each of these deeds five times indented I have set my seal; and because my seal is to many unknown, have procured the seal of the Mayor of the City of Exon to be also adjoined.

Thomas her eldest son repaired this loss, in part, by matching with one of Carminowe's daughters and heirs.

From Nicholas is descended Carew of Haccumb, who by virtue of this entail succeeded also to Hugh's portion, as deceasing issueless. From William is come Carew of Crocum in Somersetshire, and from John, Vere the now Earl of Oxford deriveth his pedigree. Alexander married Eliza-beth the daughter of Hatch, and begat John, who took to wife Thamesin, one of the daughters and heirs of Holland; their son Sir Wymond espoused Martha, the daughter of Edmund, and sister to Sir Anthony Denny. Sir Wymond had Thomas, the husband of Elizabeth Edgecumb, and they myself, linked in matrimony with Julian[a], daughter to John Arundel of Trerice, and one of the heirs to her mother, Catherine Cosewarth, who hath made me father of Richard, lately wed to Briget, daughter of John Chudleigh of Ashton in Devon.

Touching our stock in general and my family in particular, being once vainly disposed (I would it had been but once) I made this idle observa-tion.

> Carew of ancient Carru was,
>   And Carru is a plow:
> Romans the trade, Frenchmen the word,
>   I do the name avow.
> The elder stock, and we a branch,
>   At Phoebus' governing,
> From sire to son do wax and wane,
>   By thrift and lavishing.
> The sire, not valuing at due price
>   His wealth, it throws away:
> The son, by service or by match,

Repaireth this decay.
The smelling sense we sundry want,
    But want it without lack:
For 'tis no sense to wish a weal
    That brings a greater wrack.
Through nature's mark we own our babes,
    By tip of th'upper lip;
Black-bearded all the race, save mine,
    Wrong did by mothership.
The Baron's wife, Archdeacon's heir,
    Unto her younger son
Gave Antony, which down to me,
    By four descents hath run.
All which, and all their wives, exprest
    A turtle's single love,
And never did th' adventrous change
    Of double wedding prove.
We are the fifth: to swerve herefrom
    I will not, though I could;
As for my wife, God may dispose
    She shall not, though she would.
Our family transplants itself
    To grow in other shires,
And country rather makes than takes,
    As best behoof appears.
Children thrice three God hath us lent,
    Two sons, and then a maid,
By order born, of which one third
    We in the grave have laid.
Our eldest daughter widow fell
    Before our youngest born;
So do hard haps unlooked come,
    So are our hopes forlorn.
Mine trebled have in either sex
    Those which my parents got,
And yet but halved them which God
    My grandsire did allot:

Whose grace in court, rarely obtained,
   To th' youngest of those eighteen,
Three Kings of England godfathers,
   For godmother, our Queen.

The arms of our family are: Or, three lions passant, Sable; armed and langued Gules.

It exceedeth good manners to invite your longer stay at our cold harbour, and yet, for that divers strangers have, either upon cause or kindness, pretended to like well of a salt water pond there made, and others whose dwelling affordeth a semblable opportunity may (perhaps) take some light herefrom to do the like if they be so disposed, I will put myself to the pain of particularly describing it, and you may (notwithstanding) at your pleasure save the labour of perusing it, wherein I will, by the way, interlace some notes for the imitator's better instruction.

There lieth a little creek of ooze between two hills, which delivering a little fresh rillet into the sea, receiveth for recompense a large overflowing of the salt water tides. This place is deepened to a pond by casting up part of the ooze to the heads, part to the middle, and part to the sides; the upper head stoppeth out the fresh water, the lower keepeth in the salt, the middle raiseth an island for the workmen's ease, the owner's pleasure, and the fishes' succour. The ooze thus advanced, within short space through the sun and wind, changeth his former softness to a firmer hardness. Round about the pond there is pitched a frith [wattle fence] of three foot height, sloped inwards to bar any otter from issuing if he there adventure his natural theft, as it would foreclose his entrance, but lose the pastime of his hunting, if the same declined outwards. In one of the corners next the sea standeth a floodgate, to be drawn up and let down through reigles [slots] in the side posts, whose mouth is encompassed with a double frith, of two foot distance each from other and their middle space filled up with small stones. This serveth to let in the salt water and to keep in the fish when the flood-gate is taken up, and therefore you must not make the frith too close, nor the compass too little, lest they too much stop the water's passage. It riseth of equal height with the banks, and they must outreach the highest full sea mark by two foot at least; neither ought your flood-gate's foot to stand even with the pond's bottom, lest emptying the water it wholly abandon the fish, but must leave about three foot depth within. In the half circle enclosed between the flood-gate and the compass frith, there is digged a round pit of three foot diameter and four foot depth, frithed on the sides, which is continually fed with the water soaking from the said flood-gate, and serveth to keep any fish alive that you have before taken, and so to save over often drawing. The flood-gate will hold water best if his sides be walled up with cob. The pond may not carry one continual depth, but contain some shallow places to protect the smaller fish from the greater, and for them all to play in when the weather is hot. In the higher bank there is also a flood-gate to let in the fresh water during summer season, which the fish then best affecteth; the rest of the year it is carried away by a trench for avoiding divers discommodities.

Thus much for the making: now to the use. Such as have the means may best benefit themselves by letting in the salt water every tide, which is easily done in making that place where the water entereth lower than the banks and frith, and so suffering the tide to take his course forth and back without stop or attendance; and in this case you may place your flood-gate even with the floor of your pond, and never take it up but when you are disposed to view all your store. But mine lieth so high from the mouth of the haven, as I am driven to detain the last provision until the coming spring-tide have taken two days' increase, at which time the flood-gate is hoisted up, the old water let out, and the new admitted. At full sea, down goeth the flood-gate again, and there abideth until the next day minister the like occasion, and after this manner is opened and closed for six days in the whole, continuing from thenceforth other ten days unmeddled withal: to wit, eight days of the neap and two of the spring. Neither doth all this require over-long or busy pains or attendance; for if the former water be let out (saving in extreme cold weather) before any new come in, or stopped somewhat too late, it little skilleth so as on the last day you keep the advantage which the flood, then at highest, doth give you.

And all these services about my pond, together with sundry other, are performed by an old fellow whom I keep for alms, and not for his work. The best means of preventing leakage is to let three or four shovels full of earth fall softly down by the innerside of the flood-gate, which will quurt up his chinks. In winter season, six foot depth of water at least is requisite.

Now touching the fish, this is the manner: when the pilchard seiners cut the most impaired pieces out of their nets, they are bought for a trifle, and serve to make a less sein of some thirty or forty fathom length and two in depth for this purpose, wherewith, between midsummer and the end of August, when the full sea falleth in the afternoons, my people make draughts on the shallow places within harbour, and taking small fishes, cast them into the pond. They are kept and brought hither alive in a boat half full of water, which entereth through a little auger hole in the bottom, and so continueth new.

The fish thus taken are commonly bass, mullet, gilthead, whiting, smelts, fluke, plaice, and sole. The pond also breedeth crabs, eels, and shrimps, and (in the beginning) oysters grew upon boughs of trees (an Indian miracle) which were cast in thither to serve as a hover for the fish. The bass and mullet do also spawn there, but whether they overlive their breeders' ravening to any big growth I am not certain. The pond will moreover keep shot, peal, trout, and salmon in seasonable plight, but not in their wonted reddish grain. They feed on salt unmerchantable pilchard, small fish called brit and barn, tag-worms, lugs, little crabs, and the livers of beasts; the rest devour their meat, but the mullets content themselves with sucking it, and chawing of the sedge. Every morning they come to a place certain in the pond for receiving their allowed pittance, and in summer approach very near, and in the top of the water plainly discover themselves. They were first trained hereunto by throwing in their bait at the pond's mouth as they resorted thither to take pleasure of the new entering water, and are now become alike tame with those in the Sicilian river Elorus, for which Leonicus voucheth the testimony of Apollodorus. If they be absent, a knocking, like the chopping of their meat, serveth for a summons to call them, and confirmeth Pliny's assertion that fishes do hear. In the hottest summer weather they swim with the rim of the water, and in the winter keep the depth. Limy, or thick puddly water, killeth them. They grow very fast and fat, which also bettereth their taste, and delivereth them to the demander's ready use, at all seasons, seasonable.

They are taken generally by a little sein net, especially the eels in weelies, the flukes by groping in the sand at the mouth of the pond, where (about Lent) they bury themselves to spawn, and the bass and mullet by angling.

The pleasure which I took at my friends' pleasure herein, idly busied me thus to express the same:

I wait not at the lawyer's gates,
Ne shoulder climbers down the stairs;
I vaunt not manhood by debates,
I envy not the miser's fears;
    But mean in state, and calm in sprite,
    My fishful pond is my delight.

Where equal distant island views
His forced banks and otter's cage:
Where salt and fresh the pool renews
As spring and drought increase or swage:
    Where boat presents his service prest,
    And net becomes the fish's nest;

There sucking mullet, swallowing bass,
Side-walking crab, wry-mouthed fluke,
And slip-fist eel, as evenings pass,
For safe bait at due place do look,
    Bold to approach, quick to espy,
    Greedy to catch, ready to fly.

In heat the top, in cold the deep:
In spring the mouth, the mids in neap:
With changeless change by shoals they keep,
Fat, fruitful, ready, but not cheap:
    Thus mean in state, but calm in sprite,
    My fishful pond is my delight.

       And again.

Stench-loving flies, their father heat,
On mother moisture doth beget,
Who feeling force of sun too great
Their course unto some water set,
    There mean of calmy air to prove,
    Twixt cool below and warmth above.

But careless of foresight in weal,
The evening dew droploads their wing,
So forced, down-fallen, for flight to sail,
With buzzing moan their bane they sing,

Fluttering in wave, swimming in air,
That, weak to drown, and this, to bear.

While thus they can nor live nor die,
Nor water-gyved, escape away,
The fish and swallows it espy,
And both them challenge for their prey,
    The fish as caught within their toil,
    The swallows as their kindly spoil.

The fish, like swallows, mount on high,
The swallows, fish-like, dive in wave,
These finless swim, those wingless fly,
One bent their divers ventures have,
    Fish in the dry, swallows in wet,
    By kind 'gainst kind their prey to get.

Their push a bubble up doth rear,
The bubble drives the fly to brink:
So fish in vain devour the air,
Swallows in vain the water drink,
    While fly escapes; this sport I take
    Where pond doth th' Ocean captive make.

I carried once a purpose to build a little wooden banqueting house on the island in my pond, which because some other may (perhaps) elsewhere put in execution, it will not do much amiss to deliver you the plot as the same was devised for me by that perfectly accomplished gentleman, the late Sir Arthur Champernowne.

The island is square, with four rounds at the corners, like Mount-Edgecumb. This should first have been planched [boarded] over, and railed about with balusters. In the midst there should have risen a boarded room of the like fashion but lesser proportion, so to leave sufficient space between that and the rails for a walk round about. This square room should withinside have been ceiled roundwise, and in three of the places where the round joined with the square, as many windows should have been set; the fourth should have served for a door. Of the four turrets shut out by this round, one should have made a kitchen, the second a store-house to keep the fishing implements, the third a buttery, and the fourth a stair for ascending to the next loft; which next loft should have risen on the flat roof of the lower, in a round form, but of a lesser size again, so to leave a second terrace like the other. And as the square room below was ceiled round, so should this upper round room be ceiled square, to the end that where the side walls and ceiling joined, three windows and a door might likewise find their places. The void spaces between the round and square he would have turned to cupboards and boxes, for keeping other necessary utensils towards these fishing feasts.

Over against this pond lieth Beggars' Island, so called (as our neighbours relate) ever since my great grandsire, espying two of that idle occupation at a hot combat on the shore while he was rowing home from Saltash, took them into his boat and there set them on land, to try (as in a lists [joust]) the uttermost of their quarrel: which place they could not quit until the low water should enfranchise them by wading, and the respite vent out the aly fume of their fury.

About forty years ago it chanced that a boat overfreighted with people, in rowing down the river from Saltash market, was by the extreme weather sunk near to a place called Henpoint, and all the folk drowned saving one only woman named Agnes, the wife of one Cornish, whom it pleased God so to protect and direct that in her first popping up again (which most living things accustom) she espied the boat (after it had discharged his burden) risen likewise and floating by her, full of water, whereon she got hold, sat astride upon one of the sides, and by the wind and tide was unusually, and almost miraculously driven athwart the channel to a place called Wilcove, where she no sooner stepped ashore but the boat (as having done his enjoined errand) presently recommitted itself to the storm's disposition.

The woman thus freed from one peril at sea, adventured another of little less consequence at land, for being not yet thoroughly restored to her sense, she climbed up the cliff in such a steep place as the very consideration thereof doth ever sithence half amaze the beholders. But that ground was foreordained to her good, for not long after, her husband took the same with the rest of the tenement in lease, and it now serveth her for a dwelling, and many others, by her charity, for a relief.

Her said husband and their two only sons, at several times, by one kind of misfortune, found their burial in the waves.

The oysters dredged in this Lyner find a welcomer acceptance where the taste and not appetite is cater [household official who purchases food] for the stomach, than those of the adjoining Tamer, which groweth (as I conjecture) because Lyner's lesser stream leaveth them to be seasoned with a more kindly and better relished saltness.

The next parish upon this river is called Sheviock, sometimes the ancient Daunyes' inheritance and inhabitance, by whose daughter and heir the same (together with other fair possessions) descended to the Earls of Devon. In the church there lie two knights of that name, and one of their ladies by her husband's side, having their pictures embossed on their tombs in the side walls, and their arms once painted round about, but now by the malice, not of men, but of time, defaced. They are held to be father and son, and that the son, slain in our wars with France, was from thence brought home to be here interred. There runneth also a tale amongst the parishioners, how one of these Daunyes' ancestors under-took to build the church, and his wife the barn adjoining, and that casting up their accounts upon finishing of their works, the barn was found to cost three halfpence more than the church; and so it might well fall out, for it is a great barn and a little church.

In this parish standeth Crafthole, which by the high site might more fitly be termed Open-hill, a poor village but a much frequented thor-oughfare, somewhat infamous, not upon any present desert, but through an inveterate byword, viz. that it is peopled with twelve dwellings and thirteen cuckolds: for as the dwellings are more than doubled, so (I hope) the cuckolds are less than singled.

Howsoever, many wayfarers make themselves glee by putting the inhabitants in mind of this privilege, who again, especially the women (like the Campbellians in the north, and the London bargees) foreslow not to baign [drench] them (unless they plead their heels the faster) with a worse perfume than Jugurtha found fault with in the dungeon where the Romans buried him alive, to attend his languishing and miserable death.

Upon Sheviock abutteth St Germanes, the greatest parish in Cornwall, if you join to the store of people the quantity and quality of the soil, where-through it affordeth commodious dwellings to sundry ancient gentlemen and wealthy farmers; amongst which first sort I may not (without with-drawing my testimony due to virtue) omit Mr George Keckwitch of Catch-French, a house so named (by likelihood) for some former memorable, though now forgotten, accident, whose continual, large and inquisitive

126

liberality to the poor did in the late dear years extraordinarily extend itself to an inviting emulation, but beyond the apprehensive imitation of any other in the shire. He hath issue by Blanche, the daughter of Sir Frauncis Godolphin: his father George married Buller; his grandsire [gap]; their ancient dwelling was in Essex, where this gentleman enjoyeth fair possessions, and beareth for his arms Ar. two lions in bend passant Sa.cotised, G.

The church town mustereth many inhabitants and sundry ruins, but little wealth, occasioned either through abandoning their fishing trade, as some conceive, or by their being abandoned of the religious people, as the greater sort imagine; for in former times the Bishop of Cornwall's see was from St Petrock's in Bodmyn removed hither, as from hence, when the Cornish diocese united with Devon, it passed to Crediton, and lastly from thence to Excester. But this first loss received relief through a succeeding priory which at the general suppression, changing his note with his coat, is now named Port Eliot, and by the owner's charity distributeth, *pro virili* [as far as possible], the alms accustomably expected and expended at such places. Neither will it (I think) much displease you to hear how the gentleman's ancestor, of whom Master Eliot bought it, came by the same.

John Champernowne, son and heir apparent to Sir Philip, of Devon, in Henry VIII's time followed the court, and through his pleasant conceits, of which much might be spoken, won some good grace with the King. Now when the golden shower of the dissolved abbey lands rained well-near into every gaper's mouth, some two or three gentlemen, the King's servants and master Champernowne's acquaintance, waited at a door where the King was to pass forth, with purpose to beg such a matter at his hands. Our gentleman became inquisitive to know their suit: they made strange to impart it. This while, out comes the King; they kneel down, so doth master Champernowne; they prefer their petition; the King grants it; they render humble thanks, and so doth Mr Champernowne. Afterwards he requireth his share: they deny it; he appeals to the King: the King avoweth his equal meaning in the largess; whereon the overtaken companions were fain to allot him this priory for his partage.

The parish church answereth in bigness the large proportion of the parish and the surplusage of the priory, a great part of whose chancel, *anno* 1592, fell suddenly down upon a Friday very shortly after public service was ended, which heavenly favour, of so little respite, saved many persons' lives, with whom immediately before it had been stuffed, and the devout charges of the well disposed parishioners quickly repaired this ruin.

At the town's end, Cuddenbeak, an ancient house of the Bishops, from a well advanced promontory which entitled it Beak, taketh a pleasant prospect of the river.

In this parish lieth Bake, the mansion of the foreremembered Mr Robert Moyle, who married Anne, daughter of Mr Lock, as he did Mistress Vaughan, a gentlewoman suppressing her rare learning with a rarer modesty, and yet expressing the same in her virtuous life and Christian decease. John father to Robert married Agnes daughter of Seintabyn; and his father [gap] daughter of Forteskew, to whom that dwelling first descended. He beareth for his arms G. a moyle passant, Ar.

A part of this parish confineth on [borders] the main sea and offereth a fair landing place called Seaton, howbeit, by a handsome fence forbidding any foe's invasion: it is overlooked, upon the one side of the river (which there dischargeth his stream into the Ocean) by Keverel, the ancient house of the Langdons, gentlemen in former times of fair revenues, whose arms are Ar. a chevron between three bears' heads erased Sa. The house perhaps, borrowing his name of Chevereul, a French word signifying a wild goat (as those high cliffs afford them a commodious inhabitance) and on the other by Tregonnock, the dwelling of Mr Thomas Smith, who in a quiet and honest retiredness findeth that contentment which many ambitious heads far and wide do vainly seek for: he married Tremayn, his father Robert [gap] one of the daughters and heirs to Killigrew; and his son John, Priscilla, the daughter of Mr George Wadham. His arms, B. a soultier Ar., between four martlets O.

Leaving St Germans and passing through Landrake parish, in which Mr Peter Courtney hath an high seated house called Wotton, you descend to Noddetor bridge, where the river Lyner first mingleth his fresh stream with the brinish waves, touching whose name and quality, one delighted in the solitary solace of his banks, and more affecting his own recreation than hunting after any other's good liking, descanted thus:

> Who first gave Lyner's name,
> Or from what cause it came,
>   Hard 'tis for certain to express:

Experience yet directs,
By trial of effects,
    Thereat to aim, and frame a guess.
Is't, that as she thee bear'th,
So thou dost line the earth
    With purfled streams of blue and white?
Or, as a line doth guide,
So thou dost level slide,
    And throw'st into the sea thy mite?
Is't, that with twisted line
The angler doth untwine
    The fish's life, by giving breath?
Or, as the threshing lout
Rusheth his lyners out,
    So Lyner on his course rusheth?
Or, as some puppy feat,
Lineth a mastiff great,
    And getteth whelps of mongrel kind?
Lynher the sea so lines,
And stream with wave combines,
    Begetting waters freshly brined.

          Item.

When sun the earth least shadow spares,
And highest stalls in heaven his seat,
Then Lyner's pebble bones he bares,
Who like a lamb, doth lowly bleat,
    And faintly sliding every rock,
    Plucks from his foamy fleece a lock:

Before, a river, now a rill,
Before, a fence, now scarce a bound:
Children him over-leap at will,
Small beasts his deepest bottom sound.
    The heavens with brass enarch his head,
    And earth of iron makes his bed.

129

But when the milder-mooded sky
His face in mourning weeds doth wrap,
For absence of his clearest eye,
And drops tears in his centre's lap,
    Lyner 'gins lion-like to roar,
    And scorns old banks should bound him more.

Then, second sea, he rolls, and bears
Rocks in his womb, ricks on his back.
Down-born bridges, up-torn weirs,
Witness and wail his force their wrack.
    Into men's houses fierce he breaks,
    And on each stop his rage he wreaks.

Shepherd adieus his swimming flock,
The hind his whelmed harvest hope,
The strongest rampire fears his shock,
Plains scarce can serve to give him scope,
    Nor hills a bar; whereso he stray'th
    Ensue loss, terror, ruin, death.

In following the course of Lyner, you fall down by master Bond's ancient house of Earth, descended to his ancestors from the daughter and heir of that name to that of Master Wivels, newly and fairly builded, on which abutteth Mr Buller's Shillingham, not so much beholden to the owner's inhabitance as to nature's pleasant and commodious seating.

Bond married with Fountaine, his father with Fits; his arms are Ar. on a chevron Sa. three besants.

Next we take view of Trematon Castle, as it doth of the haven and country adjoining. It is, or rather was, one of the Dukes' forementioned four houses, for now all the inner buildings are sunk into ruin; only there remain the ivy-tapissed walls of the keep and base court, and a poor dwelling for the keeper of the gaol, to which prisoners are brought upon actions from all places appurtenant to that large lordship, if they cannot by suretyship discharge themselves from the bailiff's arrest.

I have received information from one averring eye-witness, that about fourscore years since, there was digged up in the parish chancel a leaden coffin, which being opened, showed the proportion of a very big man, but when the hands went about to ascertain themselves as well as their eyes, the body verified that *omnis caro pulvis* [all flesh is dust]. The party farther told me how a writing graved in the lead expressed the same to be the burial of a Duke whose heir was married to the Prince. But who it should be I cannot devise, albeit my best pleasing conjecture lighteth upon Orgerius, because his daughter was married to Edgar.

At the last Cornish commotion, Sir Richard Greynvile the elder did, with his Lady and followers, put themselves into this castle, and there for a while endured the rebels' siege, encamped in three places against it, who wanting great ordnance, could have wrought the besieged small scathe had his friends or enemies kept faith and promise. But some of those within, slipping by night over the walls with their bodies after their hearts, and those without mingling humble entreatings with rude menaces, he was hereby won to issue forth at a postern gate for parley. The while, a part of those rakehells, not knowing what honesty, and far less how much the word of a soldier imported, stepped between him and home, laid hold on his aged unwieldy body, and threatened to leave it lifeless if the enclosed did not leave their resistance. So prosecuting their first treachery against the prince with suitable actions towards his subjects, they seized on the castle and exercised the uttermost of their barbarous cruelty (death excepted) on the surprised prisoners. The seely [innocent] gentlewomen, without regard of sex or shame, were stripped from their apparel to their very smocks, and some of their fingers broken to pluck away their rings, and Sir Richard himself made an exchange from Trematon Castle to that of Launceston, with the gaol to boot.

This castle vaunteth the Lord Warden his steward by patent, Master Anthonie Rouse his bailiff by inheritance, and Richard Carew of Antony his keeper by lease. Of the ancient officers, one yet retaineth the name, though not the place, viz. Mr Porter, to whose ancestor when Vantor was lord thereof, by a deed before date gave land, lying before the gate, by the title of Russell, Janitor de Trematon, which he still enjoyeth. Mr Porter's arms are Sa. three bells Ar. a canton Erm.

It standeth in St Stephen's parish; the sheafe whereof, together with the other revenues, Mr George Wadham enjoying in the right of his wife, the daughter and heir to Master Hechins, liberally bestoweth in continual hospitality.

Master Hechins' arms are Sa. a cross fleurette, quarterly B and G between four lions' heads erased Sa. langued of the second. Mr Wadham's,

G a chevron between three roses Ar.

The same parish also compriseth Saltash, in old writings called Villa de Esse, Esse his town, and such gentlemen there have been of ancient descent and fair revenues. The word Salt is added thereunto because it standeth on the sea, and to distinguish it from other places of the same name. It is seated on the declining of a steep hill, consisteth of three streets, which every shower washeth clean, compriseth between eighty and a hundred households, underlieth the government of a mayor and his ten brethren, and possesseth sundry large privileges over the whole haven, to wit, an yearly rent of boats and barges appertaining to the harbour, anchorage of strange shipping, crowning of [acting as Coroner for] dead persons, laying of arrests, and other admiral rights [jurisdiction under the Admiralty], besides electing of burgesses for the parliaments, benefit of the passage, fore-closing of others save themselves from dredging of oysters except between Candlemas and Easter, weekly markets, half-yearly fairs, &c.

The town is of late years well increased and adorned with buildings, and the townsmen addict themselves to the honest trade of merchandise which endoweth them with a competent wealth. Some seven or eight ships belong thereunto.

It was not long since that the neighbour ministers successively bestowed their pains in preaching there on the market days, and the bordering gentlemen yielded their presence. Sermon ended, the preachers resorted to one ordinary [pub], and the gentlemen to another. This afforded commendable effects to many works of love and charity, but with the retorted blame from one to another it is now wholly given over.

Here that great carrack which Sir Frauncis Drake surprised in her return from the East Indies unloaded her freight, and through a negligent firing met with an unproper ending.

In this town also dwelleth one Grisling, deaf from a long time, who, besides his merry conceits of counterfeiting by signs (like the Roman *pantomimi* [mimes]) any kind of occupation or exercise, hath a strange quality to understand what you say by marking the moving of your lips, especially if you speak deliberately of any ordinary matter so as (contrary to the rules of nature, and yet without the help of art) he can see words as they pass forth of your mouth: and of this I have caused him to give often experiments.

And if Pliny now lived, I suppose he would afford a room in his *Natural History* to a dog of this town, who (as I have learned by the faithful report of Master Thomas Parkins) used daily to fetch meat at his house there, and to carry the same unto a blind mastiff that lay in a brake without the town: yea (that more is) he would upon Sundays conduct him thither to dinner, and the meal ended, guide him back to his couch and covert again.

I had almost forgotten to tell you that there is a well in this town, whose water will never boil peas to a seasonable softness.

At the foot of Saltash there abutteth upon the sea a rock called Ashtor, alias Ash's Tor, which is invested with the jurisdiction of a manor, and claimeth the suits of many gentlemen, as his freeholders in knights' service. Below this, there is a rock on each side of the river, the one termed the Bull, the other the Hen; that on Devon, this on Cornwall side. The Hen standeth a little distant from the shore, which giveth occasion to a pack, how between it and the land the Queen's greatest ship may sail, but it is meant of the farther distant.

Above Saltash, Cargreen, a fisher town, showeth itself, but can hardly muster a mean plight of dwellings or dwellers; so may their care be green, because their wealth is withered.

Near thereunto is Clifton, a neat seated house, appertaining to one of the Arundels, descended by a younger brother from those of Trerice: he married Hill, his father Cole.

Neither hath your eye scarcely quitted that, when it receiveth Halton, the pleasant and commodious dwelling of Mr Anthony Rouse, both which benefits he employeth to a kind and uninterrupted entertainment of such as visit him upon his not spare inviting, or their own occasions, who (without the self guilt of an ungrateful wrong) must witness that his frankness confirmeth their welcome by whatsoever means provision, the fuel of hospitality, can in the best manner supply. His ancestors were the lords of little Modbury in Devon, before the descent of times grew to a distinguishment, by the date of writings: which manor, together with other lands, through a lineal succession fell to be possessed by Raphe, Will., Raphe, John, Will., Raphe, and Raphe, whose daughter and heir Elizabeth bestowed the same, with herself, upon the family of the Dimocks. Robert, second son to the last mentioned Raphe, save one, had issue Will., who married Alice, the daughter and heir of Thomas of Edmerston. Will. had another Will. and he had John, and John again had

Will. This Will. had Roger, who upon Julian[a], sister and co-heir of John Hill of Fleet, begat John and Richard, father to the gentleman now living; and he matched with Elizabeth, daughter of Thomas Southcott, and one of the heirs to her mother, the daughter of Barnehouse: besides which, he succeeded to his Uncle John's inheritance, who deceased issueless: and being yet scarcely entered the limits of an healthful old age, seeth his pedigree extended into two farther descents. As for those outreaching man's memory, I have seen them very sufficiently verified. His arms are O. an eagle displayed B. pruning her wing, armed and langued G.

Upon the top of a creek hereby lyeth Crocadon, the mansion of Mr Trevisa, a gentleman deriving himself from the ancient and well-deserving chronicler of that name: he beareth G. a garbe O.

A mile above Halton standeth Cuttayle [Cotehele], another house of Mr Edgecumb's, so named (as we may conjecture) of the French courtaile, in English, short cut, because here the salt water course is straitened by the encroaching banks. The buildings are ancient, large, strong and fair, and appurtenanced with the necessaries of wood, water, fishing, parks, and mills, with the devotion of (in times past) a rich furnished chapel, and with the charity of alms-houses for certain poor people whom the owners used to relieve. It is reported and credited thereabouts, how Sir Richard Edgecumb the elder was driven to hide himself in those his thick woods which overlook the river, what time being suspected of favouring the Earl of Richmond's party against King Richard III, he was hotly pursued and narrowly searched for. Which extremity taught him a sudden policy, to put a stone in his cap and tumble the same into the water while these rangers were fast at his heels, who looking down after the noise and seeing the cap swimming thereon, supposed that he had desperately drowned himself, gave over their farther hunting, and left him liberty to shift away and ship over into Brittany; for a grateful remembrance of which delivery he afterwards builded in the place of his lurking, a chapel, not yet utterly decayed.

And thus having coasted the Cornish side of Plymmouth Haven, I hold it not amiss to make report of such great voyages as, by the memory of our chronicles or our own view, from this harbour took their beginning or ending.

Here the never enough commended Black Prince, attended by the Earls of Warwick, Suffolk, Salisbury and Oxford, the Lord Chandos and others, committed himself to the sea with a navy of 300 bottoms, for landing and maintaining his father's right in France; and hither, after his glorious battle at Poitiers, he returned with the captive French king and his nobles.

Here the Lady Katherine, daughter to the King of Spain and wife to our Prince Arthur, took land, at her first arrival in England. [Catherine of Aragon: to call her the wife of Henry VIII would have been treason!] Here shipped himself the Lord Darcy, sent by King Henry VIII with a lusty crew of soldiers for that Ferdinand's just assistance, against the infidels; but used by him as a stale, for the unjust conquest of Christian Navarre.

Here, mostly, have the troops of adventurers made their rendezvous for attempting new discoveries or inhabitances; as, Thomas Stukeleigh for Florida, Sir Humfrey Gilbert for Newfoundland, Sir Richard Greynvile for Virginia, Sir Martyn Frobisher and Master Davies for the North-West Passage, Sir Walter Raleigh for Guyana, &c.

Here, Count Mongomery made forth, with a more commendable meaning, than able means, or well speeding effect, for relieving the hard besieged and sore distressed Rochellers.

Here Sir Frauncis Drake first extended the point of that liquid line, wherewith (as an emulator of the sun's glory) he encompassed the world. Here Master Candish [Thomas Cavendish] began to second him with a like heroical spirit and fortunate success.

Here Don Antonio, King of Portugal, the Earls of Cumberland, Essex, and Nottingham, the Lord Warden of the Stannaries, Sir John Norrice, Sir John Hawkins (and who elsewhere, and not here?) have ever accustomed to cut sail in carrying defiance against the imaginary new monarch [King Philip] and here to cast anchor upon their return with spoil and honour.

I omit the infinite swarm of single ships and petty fleets daily here manned out to the same effect.

And here, in '88, the foreremembered Lord Admiral expected, and set forth against that heaven-threatening Armado, which, to be tainted with the shamefuller disgrace and to blaze our renown with the brighter lustre, termed itself Invincible. But I may not grow over-lascivious in extolling.

King Richard II, *anno* 5 of his reign, by Act of Parliament restrained all passengers from shipping themselves in any other ports than such as are there set down, of which Plymmouth was one.

From Plymmouth Haven, passing farther into the country, Hengsten Down presenteth his waste head and sides to our sight. This name is borrowed of Hengst, which in the Saxon signifieth a horse, and to such least dainty beasts it yieldeth fittest pasture. The country people have a byword that,

Hengsten Down, well ywrought,
Is worth London towne, deare ybought.

Which grew from the store of tin in former times there digged up, but that gainful plenty is now fallen to a scant-saving scarcity. Those works afford store of the forementioned Cornish diamonds. The neighbouring inhabitants observe also, that when the top of Hengston is capped with a cloud, the same bodeth a shower within short time after.

Roger Hoveden reporteth that about *anno* 806 a fleet of Danes arrived in West Wales, with whom the Welsh joined in insurrection against King Egbright but he gloriously discomfited them at Hengistendune, which I take to be this place (if at least West Wales may by interpretation pass for Cornwall) because the other province of that name is more commonly divided into North and South. This down is edged by Carybullock, sometimes a park of the Dukes but best brooking that name now it hath lost his quality, through exchanging deer for bullock.

A little aside from hence lieth Landwhitton, now Lawhitton, which (as I have elsewhere noted) was exempted unto Edwulff Bishop of Creditune from the Cornish diocese, to which yet, both for the temporality and spirituality, the same oweth present subjection. Marry, into what names Pontin and Coilleng there also mentioned are now metamorphized I must say *amplio* [more fully].

Those buildings commonly known by the name of Launston, and written Lanceston, are by the Cornishmen called Lesteevan (Lez in Cornish signifieth broad, and those are scatteringly erected) and were anciently termed Lanstaphadon, by interpretation St Stephen's church. They consist of two boroughs, Downevet and Newport: that (perhaps so called) of down yielding, as having a steep hill: this, of his newer erection. With them join the parishes of St Thomas and St Stephen. The parish church of Launceston itself fetcheth his title of dedication from Mary Magdalen, whose image is curiously hewed in a side of the wall, and the whole church fairly builded.

The town was first founded (saith Mr Hooker) by Eadulphus, brother to Alpsius, Duke of Devon and Cornwall, and by his being girded with a wall, argueth in times past to have carried some value.

A new increase of wealth expresseth itself in the inhabitants' late repaired and enlarged buildings. They are governed by a mayor and his scarlet-robed brethren, and reap benefit by their fairs and markets, and the county Assizes. The statute of 32 Henry VIII, which took order touching sanctuaries, endowed this town with the privilege of one, but I find it not turned to any use.

To the town there is adjoinant in site, but sequestered in jurisdiction, an ancient castle, whose steep rocky-footed keep hath his top environed with a treble wall, and in regard thereof, men say, was called Castle Terrible. The base court compriseth a decayed chapel, a large hall for holding the shire assizes, the constable's dwelling house, and the common gaol.

About sixty years past there were found certain leather coins in the castle wall, whose fair stamp and strong substance till then resisted the assault of time, as they would now of covetousness.

A little without the town were founded a friary, and *anno* 1128 an abbey, furthered by Reignald Earl of Cornwall.

About two miles distant from Launceston, Penheale mansion coasteth the highway, claiming the right of ancient demesne and sometimes appertaining to the Earls of Huntingdon, but purchased not long sithence by the late Mr George Greynvile, who descended from a younger brother of that family, and through his learning and wisdom advanced his credit to an especial good regard in his country. He married Julian[a], one of the six daughters and heirs of William Viel and Jane, the daughter to Sir John Arundel of Trerice. Richard his father took to wife one of Kelwaye's heirs; and Degory his grandfather one of the inheritors to Tregarthen: which helps, together with his own good husbandry, have endowed his son with an elder brother's livelihood. He beareth G. three restes O.

In Lezant parish hereby, Master Christopher Harris owneth a third part of Trecarell (the project and onset of a sumptuous building) as coheir to the last gentleman of that name, but admitteth no partner in the sweetly tempered mixture of bounty and thrift, gravity and pleasantness, kindness and stoutness, which grace all his actions. He beareth Sa. three croissants within a border A.

Neither may we forget Master Corington's house of Newton, old to him by succession, yet new in respect of his own antiquity: divers his ancestors have reaped the praise and reputation of a strayed carriage, howbeit one of them, through his rash but merry pranks, is to this day principally remembered by the name of the mad Corington. I have heard him deliver an observation that in eight lineal descents no one born heir of his house ever succeeded to the land. He beareth A. a saultier Sa.

Trebigh, a privileged franchise, is by his lord, Master William Wray, converted to a general welcomer of his friends and neighbours. He married the daughter of Sir William Courtney: his father the co-heir of Killigrew. he beareth Sa. a fesse between three battle-axes A.

Poole for his low and moist seat is not unaptly named, houseth Sir Jonathan Trelawny far beneath his worth and calling. He married Sir Henry Killigrew's daughter, his father the co-heir of Reskimer: his grandfather Lamellyn's inheritrix.

Poole standeth in Mynhinet parish, where Sir Jonathan hath a large privileged manor of the same name. The benefice is given by Exeter College in Oxford, none but the fellows admittable, wherethrough it hath successively been graced with three well born, well learned, and well beloved incumbents, Doctor Tremayne, Master Billet and Master Denis. Out of Sir Jonathan's house is also descended Master Edward Trelawny, a gentleman qualified with many good parts. Their arms are A. a chevron, S. between three oak-leaves vert.

Sundry other gentlemen rest beholden to this hundred for their dwellings, who in an enviable mediocrity of fortune, do happily possess themselves, and communicate their sufficient means to the service of their prince, the good of their neighbours, and the bettering of their own estate, of which sort are Mr Becket, who beareth S. a fesse, between three boars' heads coped, six crosses crosselet fichée O.; Mr Tregodecke, who beareth A. a chevron between three buckles S.; Mr Spurre, G. on a chevron O., a rose of the first, and two mullets pearnd S.; Mr Bligh, B. a griffon legreant O. armed G. between three croissants A.; Mr Lower, B. a chevron engrayled O. between three roses A.; Mr Trevisa G. a garb O.; Mr Chiverton A. a castle S standing on a hill V.; Manaton, A. on a bend S. three mullets of the field; and some others.

Stratton Hundred

Stratton Hundred extendeth the breadth of Cornwall to the north, as that of East beginneth it on the south, and therefore it shall next succeed. His circuit is slender, but his fruitfulness great, and the inhabitants' industry commendable, who reap a large benefit from their orchards and gardens, but especially from their garlic (the countryman's treacle) which they vent, not only into Cornwall, but many other shires besides.

Stratton, the only market town of this hundred, gave the same his name, and (if I mistake not) taketh it from *strata,* a street. Other memorable matter to report thereof, I find not any.

Upon one side of the town lieth Master Chamond's house and place of Launcels, so called for that it was sometimes a cell appertaining to the Abbot of Hartlond.

This gentleman's father, late deceased, received at God's hands, an extraordinary favour of long life.

He served in the office of a Justice of the Peace almost sixty years. He knew about fifty several judges of the western circuit. He was uncle, and great uncle to at least three hundred, wherein yet his uncle and neighbour, Master Greynvile, parson of Kilkhampton, did exceed him.

He married one of the daughters and heirs of Trevenner and by her saw five sons and two daughters, the youngest outstepping 40 years.

Sir John Chamond his father, a man learned in the common laws, was knighted at the Sepulchre and by dame Jane, widow to Sir John Arundell of Trerice, and daughter to Sir Thomas Greynvile, had an elder son called Thomas, whose two daughters and heirs, by Arscot, carried part of the lands to Tripcony and Trevanion, with whom they matched.

Master Chamond beareth A. a chevron between three flowers de luce, G.

In Launcels parish also standeth Norton, the house of Mr Tristram Arscot, a gentleman who by his travelling abroad in his younger years hath better enabled himself to discharge his calling at home. He took to his wife Eulalia, the widow of the wise and virtuous Mr Edmond Tremayne, and daughter of Sir John Sentleger, whose stately house of Anery in Devon he purchased, and thither hath removed his residence; he beareth party per chevron B. et E. in chief two stags' heads cabased O.

Upon the north sea, thereby, bordereth Stow, so singly called, *per eminentiam* [from its prominence], as a place of great and good mark and scope, and the ancient dwelling of the Greynviles' famous family, from whence are issued divers male branches, and whither the females have brought in a very populous kindred. Master Bernard Greinvile, son and heir to Sir Richard, is the present owner, and in a kind magnanimity treadeth the honourable steps of his ancestors.

Tonacumb, late the house of Master John Kempthorne, alias Lea, who married Katherine the daughter of Sir Peers Courtney, is by his issueless decease descended to his brother's son: he beareth A. three pineapple trees V.

Returning to the westwards, we meet with Bude, an open sandy bay, in whose mouth riseth a little hill, by every sea-flood made an island, and thereon a decayed chapel. It spareth road only to such small shipping as bring their tide with them, and leaveth them dry when the ebb hath carried away the salt water.

Upon one side hereof, Master Arundel of Trerice possesseth a pleasant-seated house and domains called Efford, alias Ebbingford, and that not unproperly, because every low water there affordeth passage to the other shore; but now it may take a new name for his better plight, for this gentleman hath, to his great charges, builded a salt-water mill athwart this bay, whose causeway serveth as a very convenient bridge to save the wayfarer's former trouble, let, and danger. It is received by tradition that his belsire, Sir John Arundel, was forewarned by I wot not what calker [astrologer] how he should be slain on the sands, for avoiding which encounter he always shunned Efford and dwelt at Trerice, another of his houses. But, as the proverb saith, *Fata viam invenient* [the Fates will find a way], and as experience teacheth men's curiosity, *Fato viam sternit* [it smooths the road for fate]. It happened, that what time the Earl of Oxford surprised St Michael's Mount by policy, and kept the same by strong hand, this Sir John Arundel was sheriff of Cornwall, wherethrough, upon duty of his office and commandment from the Prince, he marched thither with *posse comitatus* to besiege it, and there, in a skirmish on the sands, which divide the Mount from the continent, he fulfilled the effect of the prophecy with the loss of his life, and in the said Mount's chapel lieth buried.

So Cambyses lighted on Ecbatana in Egypt, and Alexander Epirot on Acheros in Italy, to bring them to their end. So Philip of Macedon, and Atis the son of Croesus found a chariot in a sword's hilt, and an iron pointed weapon at the hunting of a boar, to delude their preventive wariness. So Hamilcar supped in Syracusa, and the Prince of Wales wore a crown through Cheapside, in another sort and sense than they imagined or desired. And so Pope Gerebert and our King Henry the Fourth travelled no farther for meeting their fatal Jerusalem, than the one to a chapel in Rome, the other to a chamber in Westminster.

St Marie Wike standeth in a fruitful soil skirted with a moor, coarse for pasture and cumbrous for travellers. *Wic*, by Master Lambert, signifieth a town: by Master Camden, *stationem, vel sinum, ubi exercitus agit* [a post or safe place where an army quarters]. This village was the birthplace of Thomasine Bonaventure, I know not whether by descent or event so called, for whiles in her girlish age she kept sheep on the foreremembered moor, it chanced that a London merchant passing by saw her, heeded her, liked her, begged her of her poor parents, and carried her to his home.

In process of time, her mistress was summoned by death to appear in the other world, and her good thews [virtuous behaviour], no less than her seemly personage, so much contented her master, that he advanced her from a servant to a wife, and left her a wealthy widow. Her second marriage befell with one Henry Gall, her third and last with Sir John Percival, Lord Mayor of London, whom she also overlived. And to show that virtue as well bare a part in the desert, as fortune in the means of her preferment, she employed the whole residue of her life and last widow-hood to works no less bountiful than charitable: namely, repairing of highways, building of bridges, endowing of maidens, relieving of prison-ers, feeding and apparelling the poor, &c. Amongst the rest, at this St Mary Wike she founded a chantry and free-school, together with fair lodgings for the schoolmasters, scholars, and officers, and added twenty pound of yearly revenue for supporting the incident charges: wherein as the bent of her desire was holy, so God blessed the same with all wished success; for divers the best gentlemen's sons of Devon and Cornwall were there virtuously trained up in both kinds of divine and humane learning under one Cholwell, an honest and religious teacher, which caused the neighbours so much the rather and the more to rue that a petty smack only of popery opened a gap to the oppression of the whole, by the statute made in Edward VI's reign touching the suppression of chantries.

Such strange accidents of extraordinary advancements are verified by the ample testimony of many histories, and amongst the rest we read in Machiavel (howbeit controlled by the often reproved Jovius) that Castruccio Caestracani climbed from a baser birth to a far higher estate. For being begotten in Lucca by unknown parents, and cast out in his swaddling clouts to the wide world, he was taken up by a widow, placed by her with a clergyman her brother, given by him to a gentleman called Francesco Guinigi, and by Guinigi left tutor to his only son. From which step, his courage and wisdom raised him by degrees to the sovereignty of

Lucca, the senatorship of Rome, the special favour of the Emperor, and a near hope (only by death prevented) of subduing Florence.

Lesnewth Hundred

Lesnewith Hundred taketh his name of a parish therein (as Stratton doth of a town) memorable for nothing else. It may be derived either from *Les*, which in Cornish signifieth broad, and *newith*, which is new, as a new breadth, because it enlargeth his limits farther into Cornwall on both sides, whereas Stratton is straitened on the one by Devon; or from *Les* and *gwith*, which importeth broad ashen trees, *g* for euphonia's sake being changed into *n*.

The first place which here offereth itself to sight is Bottreaux Castle, seated on a bad harbour of the north sea, and suburbed with a poor market town, yet entitling the owner in times past with the style of a Baron, from whom by match it descendeth to the Lord Hungerford, and resteth in the Earl of Huntingdon.

The diversified rooms of a prison in the castle, for both sexes, better preserved by the inhabitants' memory than discernible by their own endurance, show the same heretofore to have exercised the same large jurisdiction.

Not far from thence, Tintogel, more famous for his antiquity than regardable for his present estate, abutteth likewise on the sea; yet the ruins argue it to have been once no unworthy dwelling for the Cornish princes. The cement wherewith the stones were laid resisteth the fretting fury of the weather better than themselves. Half the buildings were raised on the continent and the other half on an island, continued together (within men's remembrance) by a drawbridge, but now divorced by the downfallen steep cliffs on the farther side, which, though it shut out the sea from his wonted recourse, hath yet more strengthened the late island, for in passing thither you must first descend with a dangerous declining, and then make a worse ascent by a path, as everywhere narrow, so in many places through his stickleness occasioning, and through his steepness threatening, the ruin of your life with the failing of your foot. At the top, two or three terrifying steps give you entrance to the hill, which supplieth pasture for sheep and conies. Upon the same I saw a decayed chapel, a fair spring of water, a cave, reaching once, by my guide's report, some far way underground, and (which you will perhaps suspect of untruth) an hermit's grave hewn out in the rock, and serving each body's proportion for a burial. But if that in Wales carry an equal verity, the miracle will soon reap credit, for this is so sloped inwards at both ends that any tall stature shall find room by a little bending, as the short in the bottom by extending.

The farthest point of this hill is called Black Head, well known to the coasting mariners. The high cliffs are by sea inaccessible roundabouts, saving in one only place towards the east where they proffer an uneasy landing place for boats, which being fenced with a garretted wall, admitteth entrance through a gate, sometimes of iron, as the name yet continuing expresseth, and is within presently commanded by a hardly climbed hill. Under the island runs a cave thorough which you may row at full sea, but not without a kind of horror at the uncouthness of the place. Mr Camden delivereth us these verses out of an old poet, touching Tintogel:

> Est locus Abrini sinuoso littore ponti,
> Rupe situs media, refluus quem circuit aestus.
> Fulminat hic late, turrite vertice Castrum,
> Nomine Tindagium, veteres dixere Cornini.

which imports in English

> There is a place within the wind-
>   ing shore of Severn Sea
> On midst of rock, about whose foot
>   The tides turn-keeping play:
> A tow'ry topped castle here
>   Wide blazeth over all,
> Which Corineus ancient brood
>   Tindagel Castle call.

It is not laid up amongst the least vaunts of this castle, that our victorious Arthur was here begotten by the valiant Uter Pendragon upon the fair Igerna, and that without taint of bastardy, saith Merlyn, because her husband died some hours before.

Of later times, Tintogel hath kept long silence in our stories until Henry III's reign, at which time (by Matthew Paris' report) his brother Earl Richard grew into obloquy for privy receiving there, and abetting, his nephew David, against the king. After which, being turned from a palace to a prison, it restrained one John Northampton's liberty, who for abusing the same, in his unruly mayorality of London, was condemned hither as a perpetual penitentiary. A fee of ancienty belonging to this castle was cancelled as unnecessary by the late Lord Treasurer Burleigh.

One, collecting the wonders of Cornwall, followeth:

> Tintogel in his ruins vaunts,
>> Sometimes the seat of kings,
> And place which worthy Arthur bred,
>> Whose praise the Breton sings.
> A bridge these buildings joined, whom now
>> The fallen cliffs divorce,
> Yet strengthened so, the more it scorns
>> Foes' vain attempting force.
> There, cave above, entry admits,
>> But thoroughfare denies,
> Where that beneath alloweth both,
>> In safe, but ghastly wise.
> A spring there wets his head, his foot
>> A gate of iron guards;
> There measure due to each one's length
>> The hermit's grave awards.

In the midst of the wild moors of this hundred, far from any dwelling or river, there lieth a great standing water called Dosmery Pool, about a mile or better in compass, fed by no perceived spring, neither having any avoidance, until (of late) certain tinners brought an adit therefrom. The country people held many strange conceits of this pool, as, that it did ebb and flow, that it had a whirlpool in the midst thereof, and that a faggot once thrown thereinto was taken up at Foy haven, six miles distant. Wherefore, to try what truth rested in these reports, some gentlemen dwelling not far off, caused a boat and nets to be carried thither overland. Fish they caught none, save a few eels upon hooks; the pool proved nowhere past a fathom and half deep, and for a great way very shallow. Touching the opinion of ebbing and flowing, it should seem to be grounded partly upon the increase which the rain floods brought thereinto from the bordering hills (which perhaps gave also the name, for *doz* is come, and *maur* great), and the decrease occasioned by the next drought, and partly for that the winds do drive the waves to and fro upon those sandy banks. And thus the miracle of Dosmery Pool deceased.

Of this wonder he said:

> Dosmery Pool amidst the moors
> > On top stands of a hill;
> More than a mile about no streams
> > It empt, nor any fill.

Camelford, a market and fair (but not fair) town, fetcheth his derivation from the river Camel which runneth through it, and that from the Cornish word *cam*, in English crooked, as Cam, from the often winding stream. The same is incorporated with a mayoralty and nameth burgesses to the parliament, yet steppeth little before the meanest sort of boroughs for store of inhabitants, or the inhabitants' store.

Upon the river Camel, near to Camelford, was the last dismal battle strooken between the noble King Arthur and his treacherous nephew Mordred, wherein the one took his death and the other his death's wound. For testimony whereof, the old folk thereabouts will show you a stone bearing Arthur's name, though now depraved to *Atry*.

Master Camden letteth us understand that this town is sometimes termed Gaffelford; wherethrough we may mark it for the lists of a great fight between the Bretons [i.e. Britons] and Devonshire men [i.e. Saxons], which Hoveden assigneth to have been darrayned at Gavelford, and perhaps the same, which the said Master Camden voucheth out of Marianus Scotus, and describeth by these verses of an elder poet:

> *Naturam Cambela fontis*
> *Mutatam stupet esse sui, transcendit inundans*
> *Sanguineus torrens ripas, & ducit in aequor*
> *Corpora caesorum, plures natare videres,*
> *Et petere auxilium, quos undis vita reliquit.*

> The River Camel wonders that
> > His fountain's nature shows
> So strange a change, the bloody stream
> > Upswelling overflows
> His both side banks, and to the sea
> > The slaughtered bodies bears:
> Full many swim, and sue for aid,
> > While wave their life outwears.

In our forefathers' days, when devotion as much exceeded knowledge, as knowledge now cometh short of devotion, there were many bowssening places for curing of madmen, and amongst the rest, one at Alternunne in this hundred, called St Nunn's Pool, which saint's altar (it may be) by *pars pro toto* [a part for the whole] gave name to the church. And because the manner of this bowssening is not so unpleasing to hear as it was uneasy to feel, I will (if you please) deliver you the practice as I received it from the beholders.

The water running from St Nunn's well fell into a square and close walled plot, which might be filled at what depth they listed. Upon this wall was the frantic person set to stand, his back towards the pool, and from thence with a sudden blow in the breast tumbled headlong into the pond, where a strong fellow, provided for the nonce, took him and tossed him up and down, alongst and athwart the water, until the patient by foregoing his strength had somewhat forgot his fury. Then was he conveyed to the church, and certain masses sung over him; upon which handling, if his right wits returned, St Nunn had the thanks, but if there appeared small amendment he was bowssened again and again, while there remained in him any hope of life for recovery.

It may be this device took original from that master of Bedlam who (the fable saith) used to cure his patients of that impatience by keeping them bound in pools up to the middle, and so more or less after the fit of their fury.

Trigg Hundred

The name of Trigg in Cornish signifieth an inhabitant; howbeit this hundred cannot vaunt any over-large scope or extraordinary plenty of dwellings. His chief town is Bodmyn, in Cornish, *Bos venna*, commonly termed Bodman, which (by illusion if not etymology) a man might, not unaptly, turn into Badham; for of all the towns in Cornwall, I hold none more healthfully seated than Saltash, or more contagiously than this. It consisteth wholly (in a manner) of one street leading east and west wellnear the space of an eastern mile, whose south side is hidden from the sun by an high hill so nearly coasting it in most places, as neither can light have entrance to their stairs nor open air to their other rooms. Their back houses, of more necessary than cleanly service, as kitchens, stables, &c. are climbed up unto by steps, and their filth by every great shower washed down through their houses into the streets.

The other side is also overlooked by a great hill, though somewhat farther distant, and for a *corollarium*, their conduit water runneth through the churchyard, the ordinary place of burial for town and parish. It breedeth therefore little cause of marvel, that every general infection is here first admitted and last excluded; yet the many decayed houses prove the town to have been once very populous, and in that respect it may still retain the precedence, as supported by a weekly market, the greatest of Cornwall, the quarter sessions for the east division, and half yearly fairs. The jurisdiction thereof is administered by a mayor and his brethren and upon warrant of their charter they claim authority to take acknowledgment of statute bonds.

In former times the Bishop of Cornwall (as I have elsewhere related) held his see at St Petroc's in this town, until the Danish pirates, firing their palace, forced them to remove the same with their residence unto St Germans. They were succeeded by a priory and friary, which later served as a house of correction for the shire, but with greater charge than benefit, or continuance.

For other accidents, I find that Perkin Warbeck, after his landing in the west parts of Cornwall, made this town the rendezvous of his assembling forces for achieving his alike deserving and speeding enterprise against King Henry VII.

Hither also, in the last commotion, flocked the rebels from all quarters of the shire, pitching their camp at the town's end, and here they imprisoned such gentlemen as they had plucked out of their holds and houses, until the fortune of war gave verdict with the right of justice for their well deserved evil speeding.

Sir Anthony Kingston, then provost-marshal of the king's army, hath left his name more memorable than commendable amongst the townsmen, for causing their mayor to erect a gallows before his own door, upon which (after having feasted Sir Anthony) himself was hanged.

In like sort (say they) he trussed up a miller's man thereby, for that he presented himself in the other's stead, saying he could never do his master better service.

But men's tongues, readily inclined to the worst reports, have left out a part of the truth in this tale, that the rest might carry the better grace. For Sir Anthony did nothing herein as a judge by discretion, but as an officer by direction: and besides, he gave the mayor sufficient watchwords of timely warning, and large space of respite (more than which, in regard of his own peril, he could not afford) to shift for safety, if an uneschewable destiny had not haltered him to that advancement. As for the miller's man, he equalled his master in their common offence of rebellion, and therefore it deserved the praise of mercy to spare one of the two, and not the blame of cruelty to hang one for another.

I should perhaps have forgotten the free school here, maintained by her Majesty's liberality, were I not put in mind thereof through afore-halsening of this rebellion by an action of the scholars, which I will report from some of their own mouths. About a year before this stir was raised, the scholars, who accustomably divide themselves for better exploiting their pastimes, grew therethrough into two factions, the one whereof they called the old religion, the other the new. This once begun, was prosecuted amongst them in all exercises, and now and then handled with some eagerness and roughness, each party knowing, and still keeping the same companions and captain. At last one of the boys converted the spill of an old candlestick to a gun, charged it with powder and stone, and (through mischance or ungraciousness) therewith killed a calf: whereupon the owner complained, the master whipped, and the division ended.

By such tokens, sometimes wonderful, sometimes ridiculous, doth God at his pleasure foreshow future accidents: as in the planets, before the battle at Thrasimenus between Hannibal and the Romans, by the fighting together of the sun and moon. In birds, what time Brutus brought forth the remnant of his army at Philippi against Caesar and Antony, by the furious bickering between two eagles. In men, against the destruction of Jerusalem, by the encountering of chariots and armies in the air. And before Alexander's battle with Darius, first by a casual skirmish of the camp-stragglers under two captains borrowing the names of those princes, and then by Alexander's voluntary setting those captains to a single combat. Yea (to bring these examples nearer home) the like hath happened both before and sithence amongst boys in other places.

When Caesar was departed from Rome, to try the title of the world's empire with Pompey, the town boys (without any man's command) parted in twain, the one side calling themselves Pompeians, the other Caesarians; and then darrayning a kind of battle (but without arms) the Caesarians got the overhand.

A like prank under the like assumed names, and with like success and

148

boding, they played when Octavius and Anthony were, with like means, to decide the sovereignty.

And to the same purpose, Procopius affirmeth that the Samnite boys, when they drave their cattle to feeding, after their usual manner of pastime chose out amongst themselves two of the best activity and seemliness: the one they named Belisarius, general for Justinian the Emperor in Italy, the other Vitiges king of the Goths, against whom he warred. In the buckling of these counterfeit commanders it fell out that Vitiges had the worst, whom the adverse party with a jesting and cracking manner hanged up at the next tree, in earnest, but yet with no intent to kill him. This while, it happens that a wolf is descried; away run the boys; fast abides the imaginary felon, and so fast, that for want of timely rescue the breath posted out of his body, and left the same a lifeless carcass. The which notified to the Samnites, quitted the striplings (or slipstrings) of their punishment, but increased the dismay of the elder people.

A like accident befell sithence, by testimony of the ceremonious Texera, as a presage of Louis the Prince of Condé's death, 1569. Four days before which, at Xaintes, the youth of all sorts, from nine to twenty-two years age, assembled, and (of their own accord) chose two commanders: one they entitled the Prince of Condy, the other Monsieur, who then lay in the field against him. For three days' space they violently assaulted each other with stones, clubs and other weapons, until at last it grew to pistols; by one of which the imaginary Prince received a quelling wound in his head, about ten o'clock in the morning, the very hour (saith his Portugal confessor) that the Prince himself by like shot was slaughtered. The same author voucheth a semblable chance, somewhat before the siege of Rochelle, 1572, where some of the boys banded themselves as for the Mayor, and others for the King; who after six days skirmishing at last made a composition, and departed: even as that siege endured six months, and finally brake up in peace.

So doth Mercurius Gallobelgicus give us to wit, that in the year 1594 a Turkish Beglerbey of Greece, either seeking by a fore-conjecture to be ascertained himself or desirous to nuzzle [a hunting term: to accustom] the younger sort in martial exploits, led out of Alba Regalis about 600 boys aged between eleven and fourteen years and severed them into two troops, terming the one the Christian, the other the Turkish battalion. Those he directed to call upon Jesus, these upon Hala: both parts he

enjoined to bicker courageously, and egged them onward with the entice-
ment of rewards. The token is given, the forces encounter, the fight is hot.
In the end the Turks betake themselves to their heels, and Jesus' party carrieth the victory. But such occurrences do not always forego or foresig-
nify; for sometimes they fall out idle, or sometimes not at all. Howbeit,
Nicetaes Choniates taketh it very unkindly, that God would not spare
some watchword out of his prescience to the Constantinopolitans what
time Baldwin Earl of Flanders and others first assisted, and then conquered, their city.

Touching Veall the Mercurialist I have spoken in my former book.

The youthlier sort of Bodmyn townsmen use sometimes to sport themselves by playing the box with strangers, whom they summon to
Halgaver. The name signifieth the Goats' Moor, and such a place it is,
lying a little without the town, and full of quagmires. When these mates
meet with any raw servingman or other young master who may serve and
deserve to make pastime, they cause him to be solemnly arrested for his
appearance before the Mayor of Halgaver, where he is charged with wearing one spur, or going untrussed, or wanting a girdle, or some such like
felony: and after he hath been arraigned and tried with all requisite circumstances, judgment is given in formal terms and executed in some
ungracious prank or other, more to the scorn than hurt of the party condemned. Hence is sprung the proverb, when we see one slovenly apparelled, to say, 'He shall be presented in Halgaver court.'

But now and then they extend this merriment with the largest, to the
prejudice of over-credulous people, persuading them to fight with a dra-
gon lurking in Halgaver, or to see some strange matter there: which con-
cludeth at least with a training them into the mire.

Within short space after the great fame dispersed touching the rare
effects of Warwickshire wells, some idle envious head raised a bruit that
there rested no less virtue (forsooth) for healing all diseases in a plentiful
spring near unto Bodmyn, called Scarlet's Well: which report grew so far
and so fast that folk ran flocking thither in huge numbers from all quarters. But the neighbour justices, finding the abuse and looking into the
consequence, forbade the report, sequestered the spring, and suppressed
the miracle. Howbeit, the water should seem to be healthful, if not help-
ful, for it retaineth this extraordinary quality, that the same is weightier
than the ordinary of his kind, and will continue the best part of a year

without alteration of scent or taste; only you shall see it represent many colours, like the rainbow, which (in my conceit) argueth a running through some mineral vein, and therewithal a possessing of some virtue.

Aside from the town, towards the north sea, extendeth a fruitful vein of land comprising certain parishes, which serveth better than any other place in Cornwall for winter feeding, and suitably enricheth the farmers. Herethrough, sundry gentlemen have there planted their seats: as in St Kew, Master Carnsew at Bokelly: in St Endelion, Master Roscarrock at his house of the same denomination: besides Master Penkevel, Nichols, Barret, Flammock, Cavel, and divers more.

Carnsew, rightly Carndew, purporteth in Cornish a black rock, and such a one the heir owneth, which gave name to his ancient possessed manor, as the manor to his ancestors. His house, Bokelly, may be derived from *both*, in Cornish a goat, and *kelly*, which is lost; and the goat he giveth for his arms. This gentleman's father married the daughter of Fits in Devon, and left behind him three sons, Richard, Matthew, and William, with two daughters, those brought up in learning and experience abroad, these in virtue and modesty at home: the fruits whereof they taste and express in a no less praiseworthy than rare-continuing concord, having (not through any constraining necessity or constraintive vow) but on a voluntary choice, made their elder brother's mansion a college of single living and kind entertaining. Amongst whom I may not omit the youngest brother, whose well qualified and sweet pleasing sufficiency draweth him out from the cloister to converse with and assist his friends, and to whose sound judgment I owe the thankful acknowledgment of many corrected slippings in these my notes. The arms of this family are thus blazoned, S. a goat passant A., attired and trepped O.

Roscarrock, in Cornish, meaneth 'a flower and a rock' in English. Roses are his arms, and the north rocky cliffs which bound his domains perhaps added the rest. The heir hath issue by the daughter of Trevanion. His father married the sole inheritrix to Pentire, whose dwelling, Pentuan, is seated on the south sea, so as he might make use of either climate for his residence. The family is populous, but of them two brothers, Hugh for his civil carriage and kind hospitality, and Nicholas for his industrious delight in matters of history and antiquity, do merit a commending remembrance. They bear A. a chevron between two roses G. and a sea-tench nayante proper.

The little parish called Temple skirteth this hundred on the waste side thereof, a place exempted from the bishop's jurisdiction, as once appertaining to the Templars, but not so from disorder; for if common report communicate with truth, many a bad marriage bargain is there yearly slubbered up.

Hundred of West

With Trig Hundred, on the south side confineth that of West, but taketh his name from the relation which it beareth to that of East. The circuit thereof is not so large as fruitful.

In entering the same we will first pitch at the Looes, two several corporations distinguished by the addition of East and West, abutting upon a navigable creek, and joined by a fair bridge of many arches. They took that name from a fresh river which there payeth his tribute to the sea, and the river (as I conjecture) from his low passage between steep coasting hills, for Loo and low, after the Cornish pronunciation, do little differ.

East-Loo voucheth less antiquity, as lately incorporated, but vaunteth greater wealth, as more commodiously seated; yet the foundation of their houses is grounded on the sand, supporting (naytheless) those poor buildings with a sufficient stableness. Their profit chiefly accrueth from their weekly markets, and industrious fishing with boats of a middle size, able to brook but not cross the seas; howbeit, they are not altogether destitute of bigger shipping, amongst which, one hath successively retained the name of the *George of Loo*, ever since the first so called did, a great while sithence, in a furious fight take three French men of war.

The town towards the sea is fenced with a garretted wall, against any sudden attempt of the enemy.

West-Loo mustereth an endowment with the like means, but in a meaner degree, and hath of late years somewhat relieved his former poverty.

Almost directly over against the barred haven of Loo extendeth St George's Island, about half a mile in compass and plentifully stored with conies. When the season of the year yieldeth opportunity a great abundance of sea-fowl breed upon the strond, where they lay and hatch their eggs without care of building any nests, at which time repairing thither, you shall see your head shadowed with a cloud of old ones, through their diversified cries witnessing their general dislike of your disturbance, and your feet pestered with a large number of young ones, some formerly, some newly, and some not yet disclosed; at which time (through the leave and kindness of Master May, the owner) you may make and take your choice. This gentleman's arms are G. a chevron vary between three crowns.

The middle market town of this hundred is Liskerd. *Les* in Cornish is broad, and *ker* is gone. Now, if I should say that it is so called because the wideness of this hundred here contracteth the traffic of the inhabitants, you might well think I jested, neither dare I avow it in earnest. But whencesoever you derive the name, hard it is in regard of the antiquity to deduce the town and castle from their first original; and yet I will not join hands with them who term it *Legio*, as founded by the Romans, unless they can approve the same by a Roman faith.

Of later times, the castle served the Earl of Cornwall for one of his houses, but now, that latter is worm-eaten out of date and use. Coinages, fairs, and markets (as vital spirits in a decayed body) keep the inner parts of the town alive, while the ruined skirts accuse the injury of time and the neglect of industry.

St Cleer parish, coasting Liskeard, brooketh his name by a more piercing than profitable air, which in those open wastes scoureth away thrift as well as sickness. Thither I rode to take view of an antiquity called The Other Half Stone, which I found to be thus: there are two moor stones pitched in the ground very near together, the one of a more broad than thick squareness about eight foot in height, resembling the ordinary spill of a cross, and somewhat curiously hewed with diaper work. The other cometh short of his fellow's length by the better half, but wellnear doubleth it in breadth and thickness, and is likewise handsomely carved. They both are mortised in the top, leaving a little edge at the one side as to accommodate the placing of somewhat else thereupon. In this latter are

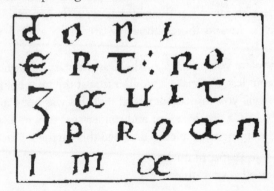

graved certain letters, which I caused to be taken out, and have here inserted for abler capacities than mine own to interpret.

Why this should be termed The Other Half Stone I cannot resolve with myself, and you much less. Howbeit, I haltingly aim it may proceed from one of these respects: either because it is the half of a monument whose other part resteth elsewhere, or for that it meaneth, after the Dutch phrase and their own measure, a stone and half. For in Dutch, *Ander halb* (another half) importeth one and a half, as *Sesqui alter* doth in Latin. It should seem to be a bound stone, for some of the neighbours observed to me that the same limiteth just the half way between Excester and the land's end, and is distant full fifty miles from either.

Not far hence, in an open plain, are to be seen certain stones, somewhat squared, and fastened about a foot deep in the ground, of which some six or eight stand upright in proportionable distance; they are termed The Hurlers. And a like strange observation taketh place here as at Stone-henge, to wit, that a redoubled numbering never eveneth with the first. But far stranger is the country people's report that once they were men, and for their hurling upon the Sabbath, so metamorphosed. The like whereof I remember to have read touching some in Germany (as I take it), who for a resemblable profanation with dancing, through a priest's accursing continued it on a whole year together.

Almost adjoining hereunto is a heap of rocks which press one of a less size fashioned like a cheese, and therethrough termed Wringcheese.

I know not well, whether I may refer to the parish of St Neot in this Hundred, that which Matthew of Westminster reporteth of King Alfred, namely how coming into Cornwall on hunting, he turned aside, for doing his devotion, into a church where St Guerir and St Neot made their abode (*quaere*, whether he mean not their burials) or rather so resolve, because Asser so delivers it, and there found his orisons seconded with happy effect.

Next, I will relate you another of the Cornish natural wonders, viz. St Kayne's Well; but lest you make a wonder first at the saint before you take notice of the well, you must understand that this was not Cain the man-queller, but one of a gentler spirit and milder sex, to wit, a woman. He who caused the spring to be pictured, added this rhyme for an exposition:

> In name, in shape, in quality,
> This well is very quaint;

The name, to lot of Kayne befell,
  No over-holy saint.
The shape, four trees of divers kind,
  Withy, oak, elm, and ash,
Make with their roots an arched roof,
  Whose floor this spring doth wash.
The quality, that man or wife
  Whose chance or choice attains
First of this sacred stream to drink
  Thereby the mastery gains.

In this hundred, the rubble of certain mines and ruins of a fining house convince Burchard Craneigh the Dutchman's vain endeavour in seeking of silver ore. Howbeit, he afterwards lighted on a thriftier vein, of practising physic at London, where he grew famous by the name of Doctor Burcot.

Killigarth, being interpreted in English, signifieth, He hath lost his griping, or reaching; and by his present fortune (in some sort) justifieth that name: for the same hath lately forgone Sir William Bevill, whom it embraced as owner and inhabitant, by his sudden death, and is passed into the possession of the fair lady his widow, by her husband's conveyance.

It yieldeth a large view of the south coast, and was itself in Sir William's lifetime much visited through his frank invitings. The mention of this knight calleth to my remembrance a sometimes uncouth servant of his, whose monstrous conditions partly resembled that Polyphemus described by Homer and Virgil, and lively imitated by Ariosto in his *Orco*: or rather that Egyptian Polyphagus, in whom (by Suetonius' report) the Emperor Nero took such pleasure. This fellow was taken up by Sir William under a hedge in the deepest of winter, wellnear starved with cold and hunger. He was of stature mean, of constitution lean, of face freckled, of composition well proportioned, of diet naturally spare, and cleanly enough; yet at his master's bidding he would devour nettles, thistles, the pith of artichokes, raw and living birds and fishes with their scales and feathers, burning coals and candles, and whatsoever else, however unsavoury, if it might be swallowed: neither this a little, but in such quantity as it often bred a second wonder how his belly could contain so much, yet could no man at any time discover him doing of that which necessity of nature requireth. Moreover he would take a hot iron out of the fire with his bare hand, never changed his apparel but by constraint, and used to lie in straw with his head down and his heels upwards. Spare he was of speech, and instead of half his words used this term *Size*, as I will size him, for strike him; he is a good size, for man, &c. Over-sleeping, or some other accident, made him to lose a day in his account of the week, so as he would not believe but that Sunday was Saturday, Saturday Friday, &c. To Sir William he bare such faithfulness that he would follow his horse like a spaniel, without regard of way or weariness, wait at his chamber door the night time, suffering none to come near him, and perform what-soever he commanded, were it never so unlawful or dangerous.

On a time, his master, expecting strangers, sent him with a pannier to his cater at the sea side to fetch some fish. In his way he passed by a river whereinto the tide then flowed, and certain fishermen were drawing their nets, which after John Size had a while beheld, he casts to have a share amongst them for his master. So into the water he leaps, and there for the space of a flight-shoot wadeth and walloweth (for swim he could not), sometimes up and sometimes down, carrying his pannier still before him, to his own extreme hazard of drowning and the beholders' great pitying, until at last all wet and wearied, out he scrambleth, and home he hieth with a bitter complaint to his master of his ill fortune, that he could not catch some fish as well as the rest where so much was going. In this sort he continued for divers years, until (upon I wot not what freak or unkind-ness) away he gets and abroad he rogues, which remitter brought him in the end to his fore-deferred and not avoided destiny; for as under a hedge he was found pining, so under a hedge he found his miserable death through penury.

Sir William's father married the daughter of Militon: his grandfather the daughter and heir of Bear, whose livelihood repaired what the elder brother's daughters had impaired. The Bevils' arms are A. a bull passant G. armed and tripped O.

In the same parish where Killigarth is seated, Master Murth inheriteth a house and demesnes. He married Treffry, his father Tregose. One of their ancestors within the memory of the next neighbour to the house, called Prake (burdened with 110 years' age) entertained a British [Breton] miller, as that people, for such idle occupations, prove more handy than our own. But this fellow's service befell commodious in the worst sense. For when, not long after his acceptance, wars grew between us and France, he stealeth over into his country, returneth privily back again with a French crew, surpriseth suddenly his master and his guests at a Christmas supper, carrieth them speedily unto Lantreghey and forceth the gentleman to redeem his enlargement with the sale of a great part of his revenues.

A little to the westward from Killigarth, the poor harbour and village of Polpera coucheth between two steep hills, where plenty of fish is vented to the fish drivers, whom we call jowters.

The warmth of this hundred, siding the south, hath enticed many gentlemen here to make choice of their dwellings, as Mr Buller, now sheriff, at Tregarrick, sometimes the Wideslades' inheritance, until the father's rebellion forfeited it to the Prince, and the Prince's largess rewarded therewith his subjects. Wideslade's son led a walking life with his harp to gentlemen's houses, wherethrough, and by his other active qualities, he was entitled Sir Tristram; neither wanted he (as some say) a *belle Isound*, the more aptly to resemble his pattern.

Master Buller married the daughter of one Williams, a Counsellor at Law in Devon: his father, a younger branch of the ancient stock, planted in Somersetshire, took to wife the widow of Courtney, and daughter and heir to Trethurffe; by whose dower, and his own endeavour, he purchased and left to his son fair possessions, but not encumbered with titles, which drave this gentleman to salve them all by new compositions with the pretenders: and for compassing the same, to get an extraordinary experience in husbandry. his ancestors bare S. on a plain cross A. quarter pierced four eagles of the field.

At St Winow inhabiteth Mr Thomas Lower, commendable through his double provision against the wars, as having both furnished himself with great ordnance for private defence of the country, and thrust forth his sons to be trained in martial knowledge and exercises for the public service of the country.

His wife was one of the Reskimers' daughters and heirs: his mother, the daughter of Treffry: his house descended to his ancestor by marriage with Upton. He beareth B. a chevron engrayled O. between three roses A.

Laureast [Lanrest] is the inheritance of Mr John Harris, a gentleman employing his sound judgement and other praiseworthy parts to the service of his prince and country, and the good of his friends and himself. His wife was daughter and heir to Hart: his mother sister to Mr Christopher Harris,which (by his uncle's yet want of issue) entitleth him to a fair expectancy. He beareth S. three croissants within a border A.

Treworgy is owned by Mr Kendal, and endowed with a pleasant and profitable fishing and command of the river, which flitteth under his house. He married with Buller: his mother was daughter to Moyle of Bake, and beareth A. a chevron between three dolphins S.

Master Glyn of Glynfoord manifesteth, by this compounded name, the antiquity of his descent, and the ordinary passage there over the Foy River. The store of salmons which it affordeth caused his ancestors to take the salmon spears for their arms: for he beareth A. a chevron between three salmon spears S.

Sundry more gentlemen this little Hundred possesseth, and possession-eth, as Code, who beareth A. a chevron G between three crows; May, G. a chevron vary between three crowns; Achym, A. a maunche maltaile S. within a border of the first, charged with cinquefoil, as the second grills, &c. But want of information, and lothness to wax tedious, maketh me far-dle up these and omit the rest.

It is hemmed in on the west by the east side of Foy haven, at whose mouth standeth Hall, in Cornish, a moor, and (perhaps) such it was before better manurance reduced it to the present fruitfulness. The same descended to Sir Reignald Mohun from his ancestors, by their match with the daughter and heir of Fits-Williams, and (amongst other commodities) is appurtenanced with a walk which, if I could as plainly show you as myself have oftentimes delightfully seen it, you might and would avow the same to be a place of diversified pleasings. I will therefore do my best to trace you a shadow thereof, by which you shall (in part) give a guess at the substance.

It is cut out in the side of a steep hill whose foot the salt water washeth, evenly levelled to serve for bowling, floored with sand for soaking up the rain, closed with two shorn hedges, and banked with sweet scenting flow-ers. It wideneth to a sufficient breadth for the march of five or six in front, and extendeth to not much less than half a London mile; neither doth it lead wearisomely forthright, but yieldeth varied and yet not over-busy turnings as the ground's opportunity affordeth, which advantage increaseth the prospect, and is converted on the foreside into platforms for the planting of ordnance and the walkers' sitting, and on the back part into summer-houses for their more private retreat and recreation.

In passing along, your eyes shall be called away from guiding your feet, to descry by their farthest kenning the vast ocean sparkled with ships that continually this way trade forth and back to most quarters of the world. Nearer home, they take view of all sized cocks, barges, and fisherboats, hovering on the coast. Again, contracting your sight to a narrower scope, it lighteth on the fair and commodious haven, where the tide daily presenteth his double service of flowing and ebbing, to carry and recarry whatsoever the inhabitants shall be pleased to charge him withal, and his creeks (like a young wanton lover) fold about the land with many embracing arms.

This walk is guarded upon the one side by Portruan, on the other by Bodyneck, two fishing villages; behind, the rising hill beareth off the cold northern blasts; before, the town of Foy subjecteth his whole length and breadth to your overlooking; and directly under you ride the home and foreign shipping, both of these in so near a distance, that without troubling the passer, or borrowing Stentor's voice, you may from thence not only call to, but confer with any in the said town or shipping.

Monsieur la Noüe noteth that in the great hall of justice at Paris there is no room left for any more images of the French kings, which some prophetically interpreted to signify a dissolution of that line, if not of the monarchy. But this halsening, the present flourishing state of that kingdom utterly convinceth of falsehood. A far truer foretoken, touching the Earl of Devon's progeny, I have seen at this place of Hall, to wit, a kind of faggot, whose age and painting approveth the credited tradition that it was carefully preserved by those noble men, but whether upon that prescience or no, there mine author fails me. This faggot, being all one piece of wood, and that naturally grown, is wrapped about the middle part with a bond, and parted at the ends into four sticks, one of which is again subdivided into other twain. And in semblable manner the last Earl's inheritance accrued unto four Cornish gentlemen, Mohun, Trelawny, Arundell of Talverne, and Trethurffe: and Trethurffe's portion, Courtney of Ladocke, and Vivian do enjoy, as descended from his two daughters and heirs.

Sir Reignald Mohun is widower of two wives; the one, daughter to Sir Henry Killigrew, the other to Sergeant Heale; his father, Sir William, married first the daughter of Horsey, and one of the heirs, by common law, to Sir John her late brother; and next, the widow of Trelawny, who, overliving him, enjoyeth this Hall as part of her jointure; a lady gracing her dignity with her virtue, and no less expressing than professing religion.

Reignald, father to Sir William, wedded the daughter of Sir William Trevanion. The arms of the Mohuns are O. a cross engrayled S.

Powder Hundred

Some impute the force of powder unto this, that the same is converted at an instant from an earthy substance to a fiery, and from the fire into air, every of which changes requireth a greater enlargement one than other, wherefore it finding a bar over, under, and on the back and sides by the piece's strong imprisonment, by consequence breaketh forth with a sudden violence at the mouth where the way is least stopped, and driveth before it the unsettled obstacle of the bullet, imparting thereunto a portion of his fury. To which (through want of a probable etymon) I may in part resemble the Hundred of Powder, not only for the name's sake, but also because this parcel of the Cornish earth extendeth itself wider and compriseth more parishes than any other hundred of the shire, as stretching east and west from Foy to Falmouth, and south and north wellnear from one sea to the other.

In describing the same we must begin where we left, to wit, at Foy Haven, in Cornish, *Foath*. It receiveth this name of the river, and bestoweth the same on the town. His entrance is guarded with blockhouses, and that on the town's side, as also the town itself, fortified and fenced with ordnance. The commendation of which industry is principally due to the providence and direction of Mr William Treffry, a gentleman that hath vowed his rare gifts of learning, wisdom, and courage to the good of his country, and made proof thereof in many occurrents, and to whose judicious corrections these my notes have been not a little beholden. His fair and ancient house, castle-wise builded and sufficiently flanked, overlooketh the town and haven with a pleasant prospect, and yet is not excluded from the healthful air and use of the country, which occasioned his ancestors (though endowed elsewhere with large revenues, of their own and wives' inheritance) for many descents to make here their ordinary residence, as is witnessed by their tombstones which I have seen in the church. One of them, about 145 years sithence, valiantly defended this his dwelling against the French, what time they had surprised the rest of the town.

He married one of Tremayne's heirs: his father the heir of Tresithny: his grandfather, the daughter of Killigrew: and beareth S. a chevron between three hawthorns A. But I will return to the town. During the warlike reigns of our two valiant Edwards, the first and third, the Foyens addicted themselves to back their Princes' quarrel by coping with the enemy at sea, and made return of many prizes, which purchases having advanced them to a good estate of wealth, the same was (when the quieter-conditioned times gave means) heedfully and diligently employed and bettered by the more civil trade of merchandise; and in both these vocations they so fortunately prospered, that it is reported sixty tall ships did at one time belong to the harbour, and that they assisted the siege of Calais with forty-seven sail.

Hereon, a full purse begetting a stout stomach, our Foyens took heart at grass, and chancing about that time (I speak upon the credit of tradition) to sail near Rye and Winchelsea, they stiffly refused to veil their bonnets at the summons of those towns, which contempt (by the better enabled seafarers reckoned intolerable) caused the ripiers [longshoremen] to make out with might and main against them, howbeit, with a more hardy onset than happy issue, for the Foy men gave them so rough entertainment at their welcome that they were glad to forsake patch without bidding farewell, the merit of which exploit entitled them Gallants of Foy. And (it may be) they sought to eternize this memorable fact after the Greek and Roman manner, by investing the town of Golant with that name; notwithstanding, *quaere* whether a causeless ambition in the posterity turned not rather Golant into Gallant, for their greater glory.

Once, the townsmen vaunt, that for rescuing certain ships of Rye from the Normans in Henry III's time they bear the arms, and enjoy part of the privileges appertaining to, the Cinque Ports, whereof there is some memory in their chancel window, with the name of Fisart Bagga, their principal commander in that service. Moreover, the prowess of one Nicholas, son to a widow near Foy, is descanted upon, in old three mans' songs, namely, how he fought bravely at sea, with John Dory (a Genowey, as I conjecture) set forth by John the French king, and (after much bloodshed on both sides) took and slew him, in revenge of the great ravine and cruelty which he had fore-committed upon the Englishmen's goods and bodies. Yet their so often good success sometimes tasted the force of crosser speeding; for Thomas Walsingham telleth us that Sir Hugh Calveley and Sir Thomas Percy, deputed to guard the sea by Richard II, *anno* 1379, chanced there to meet a Cornish barge, belonging to Foy harbour, which having worn out his victuals and time, limited for the like service, was then sailing homewards, neither would be entreated by those knights to join company with them: howbeit they bought this refusal very dear. For no sooner was the English fleet passed out of sight but that a Flemish man-of-war lighted upon them and (after a long and strong resistance) overmastered them as well, at last in force, as they did at first in number, took the barge, sunk it, and slaughtered all the sailors, one only boy excepted, who in the heat of the bickering, seeing which way the game would go, secretly stole aboard the Fleming, and closely hid himself amongst the ballast. Over a while, this pirate cast anchor in an English harbour, where the boy, hearing his countryman's voice, that were come aboard, riseth from his new burial, bewrayeth the fact and so wrought means for their punishment, and his own delivery.

Not long after, our Foy gallants, unable to bear a low sail, in their fresh gale of fortune, began to skum the seas with their often piracies (avowing themselves upon the Earl of Warwick, whose ragged staff is yet to be seen portrayed in many places of their church steeple, and in divers private houses), as also to violate their duty at land by insolent disobedience to the Prince's officers, cutting off (among other pranks) a pursuivant's ears; whereat King Edward the Fourth conceived such indignation as he sent commissioners unto Lostwithiel (a town thereby), who under pretence of using their service in sea affairs, trained thither the greatest number of the burgesses; and no sooner come than laid hold on, and in hold, their goods were confiscated, one Harrington executed, the chain of their haven removed to Dartmouth, and their wonted jollity transformed into a sudden misery, from which they strived a long time in vain to relieve themselves, but now of late years do more and more aspire to a great amendment of their former defects, though not to an equal height of their first abundance.

Where I may not pass in silence the commendable deserts of Master Rashleigh the elder, for his industrious judgment and adventuring in trade and merchandise first opened a light and way to the townsmen's new thriving, and left his son large wealth and possessions, who (together with a daily bettering his estate) converteth the same to hospitality and other actions fitting a gentleman well affected to his God, Prince, and Country. He married the daughter of Bonithon, his father of Lanyne, and beareth S. a plain cross between two croissants A.

Anno 28 Henry VI there was an Act of Parliament made to restrain the abuses of sea-officers, in wrong exactions at Foy, and some other havens.

The Lord of Pomier, a Norman, encouraged by the civil wars wherewith our realm was then distressed, furnished a navy within the river of Seine and with the same, in the night, burned a part of Foy, and other houses confining: but upon approach of the country's forces, raised the next day by the Sheriff, he made speed away to his ships, and with his ships to his home.

In a highway near this town, there lieth a big and long moor stone containing the remainder of certain engraved letters, purporting some memorable antiquity, as it should seem, but past ability of reading. Not many years sithence, a gentleman dwelling not far off was persuaded by some information or imagination that treasure lay hidden under this stone. Wherefore, in a fair moonshine night, thither with certain good fellows he hieth to dig it up; a working they fall, their labour shorteneth, their hope increaseth, a pot of gold is the least of their expectation. But see the chance; in midst of their toiling the sky gathereth clouds, the moonlight is overcast with darkness, down falls a mighty shower, up riseth a blustering tempest, the thunder cracketh, the lightning flasheth; in conclusion, our money-seekers washed instead of laden, or laden with water instead of yellow earth, and more afraid than hurt, are forced to abandon their enterprise and seek shelter of the next house they could get into. Whether this proceeded from a natural accident or a working of the devil I will not undertake to define. It may be God giveth him such power over those who begin a matter upon covetousness to gain by extraordinary means, and prosecute it with a wrong in entering and breaking another man's land without his leave, and direct the end thereof to the prince's defrauding, whose prerogative challengeth these casualties.

A little beyond Foy, the land openeth a large sandy bay for the sea to overflow, which, and the village adjoining are therethrough aptly termed Trewardreth, in English the Sandy Town. Elder times, of more devotion than knowledge, here founded a religious house which in King Henry VIII's reign underwent the common downfall.

I have received credible information that some three years sithence certain hedgers dividing a close on the seaside hereabouts, chanced in their digging upon a great chest of stone artificially joined, whose cover they (over-greedy for booty) rudely brake, and therewithal a great earthen pot enclosed, which was gilded and graved with letters defaced by this mis-adventure, and full of a black earth, the ashes (doubtless) as that the *urna* of some famous personage.

Upon a side of this bay, one Mr Peter Bevill first began the experiment of making a saltwater pond, induced thereunto by observing that the high summer tides brought with them young basses and mullets, whom at their ebbing they left behind in little pits of the uneven ground, where they would live for many weeks without any revisitation of the sea: who, as he bettered this natural pattern, so did I his artificial, but yet with a thankful acknowledgment, by whom I have profited.

Lostwithiel should seem to fetch his original from the Cornish *Loswithiall*, which in English soundeth a Lion's Tail; for as the Earl of this province gave the lion in arms, and the lion's principal strength (men say) consisteth in his tail, so this town claimeth the precedence as his lord's chiefest residence and the place which he entrusted with his exchequer, and where his weightier affairs were managed. Mayoralty, markets, fairs, and nomination of burgesses for the parliament it hath in common with the most, coinage of tin only with three others, but the gaol for the whole Stannary and keeping of the county courts, itself alone. Yet all this can hardly raise it to a tolerable condition of wealth and inhabitance. Wherefore I will detain you no longer than until I have showed you a solemn custom in times past here yearly observed, and only of late days discontinued, which was thus:

Upon little Easter Sunday the freeholders of the town and manor, by themselves or their deputies, did there assemble: amongst whom, one (as it fell to his lot by turn) bravely apparelled, gallantly mounted, with a crown on his head, a sceptre in his hand, a sword borne before him, and dutifully attended by all the rest on horseback, rode through the principal street to the church; there the curate in his best beseen solemnly received him at the churchyard stile and conducted him to hear divine service; after which he repaired with the same pomp to a house foreprovided for that purpose, made a feast to his attendants, kept the table's end himself, and was served with kneeling, assay, and all other rites due to the estate of a prince: with which dinner the ceremony ended, and every man returned home again. The pedigree of this usage is derived from so many descents of ages that the cause and author outreach remembrance: howbeit, these circumstances offer a conjecture that it should betoken the royalties appertaining to the honour of Cornwall.

Mr William Kendal's hospitality, while he lived and here kept house, deserveth a special remembrance, because for store of resort and frankness of entertainment it exceeded all others of his sort.

This town, *anno* 11 Henry VII was by act of parliament assigned to keep the public weights and measures ordained for the county.

Lostwithiel subjected itself to the command of Restormel Castle, *alias* Lestormel, sometimes the Duke's principal house. It is seated in a park upon the plain neck of a hill, backed to the westward with another somewhat higher, and falling every way to end in a valley watered by the fishful river of Foy. His base court is rather to be conjectured than discerned by the remnant of some few ruins, amongst which an oven of fourteen feet largeness through his exceeding proportion proveth the like hospitality of those days. The inner court, grounded upon an entrenched rock, was formed round, had his utter wall thick, strong, and garretted, his flat roof covered with lead, and his large windows taking their light inwards. It consisted of two stories, besides the vaults, and admitted entrance and issue by one only gate fenced with a portcullis. Water was conveyed thither by a conduit from the higher ground adjoining. Certes, it may move compassion that a palace so healthful for air, so delightful for prospect, so necessary for commodities, so fair (in regard of those days) for building, and so strong for defence, should in time of secure peace, and under the protection of his natural princes, be wronged with those spoilings than which it could endure no greater at the hands of any foreign and deadly enemy. For the park is disparked, the timber rooted up, the conduit pipes taken away, the roof made sale of, the planchings rotten, the walls fallen down, and the hewed stones of the windows, dourns and clavels [door frames and hearth lintels], plucked out to serve private buildings; only there remaineth an utter defacement to complain upon this unregarded distress. It now appertaineth by lease to Master Samuel, who married Halse; his father (a wise and pleasant-conceited gentleman) matched with Tremayne.

After we have quitted Restormel, Roche becomes our next place of sojourn, though hardly inviting with promise of any better entertainment than the name carrieth written in his forehead, to wit, a huge, high, and steep rock seated in a plain, girded on either side with (as it were) two substitutes, and meritorious (no doubt) for the hermit who dwelt on the top thereof, were it but in regard of such an uneasy climbing to his cell and chapel, a part of whose natural walls is wrought out of the rock itself.

Near the foot of Roche there lieth a rock, level with the ground above, and hollow downwards with a winding depth, which containeth water, reported by some of the neighbours to ebb and flow as the sea. Of these, as another Cornish wonder:

> You neighbour-scorners, holy-proud,
>> Go people Roche's cell,
> Far from the world, near to the heavens,
>> There, hermits, may you dwell.
> Is't true that spring in rock hereby
>> Doth tide-wise ebb and flow?
> Or have we fools with liars met?
>> Fame says it; be it so.

From hence ascending easily the space of a mile, you shall have won the top of the Cornish archbeacon Hainborough, which (as little to great) may for prospect compare with Rama in Palestina, Henius in Medica, Collalto in Italy, and Snaefell in the Isle of Man: for if the weather's darkness bound not your eyesight, within his ordinary extent you shall thence plainly discern, to the eastward, a great part of Devon, to the west, very near the land's end, to the north and south, the ocean and sundry islands scattered therein; wherethrough it also passeth for a wonder.

> Haynborough's wide prospect, at once
>> Both feeds and gluts your eye,
> With Cornwall's whole extent, as it
>> In length and breadth doth lie.

At Ladocke in this hundred, dwelleth Master Peter Courtney, who doubly fetcheth his pedigree from that honourable stock, and embraceth the contentment of a quiet private life, before the public charge in his country due to his calling, and to which long sithence he hath been called. His father married (as I have showed) the daughter and co-heir of Trethurffe, himself Reskimer's, his son the daughter of Saintabyn: he beareth O. three torteaux, and a file with as many lambeaux, B.

Leo Afer, in the delightful and approved description of his country, telleth us of a blind guide who would readily and safely conduct strange travellers over the huge deserts with which that region aboundeth, and that the means he used was in certain distances to smell at the sand, which gave him perfect notice of the places.

Likewise Lewes Guicciardin, in his book of the Netherland, maketh report of one Martyn Catelyn, born at Wervicke in Flanders, who, falling blind before he attained two years age, grew notwithstanding, by his own industry, without any teacher, to such a perfection in timber handicraft as he could not only turn and make virginals, organs, violins and suchlike instruments with great facility, order and proportion, but also tune, and handsomely play upon them, and besides, devised many serviceable tools for his science.

These examples I thrust out before me to make way for a not much less strange relation touching one Edward Bone, sometimes servant to the said Master Courtney – which fellow (as by the assertion of divers credible persons I have been informed) deaf from his cradle and consequently dumb, would yet be one of the first to learn and express to his master any news that was stirring in the country; especially if there went speech of a sermon within some miles distance, he would repair to the place with the soonest, and setting himself directly against the preacher, look him steadfastly in the face while his sermon lasted; to which religious zeal his honest life was also answerable, for as he shunned all lewd parts himself, so if he espied any in his fellow servants (which he could and would quickly do) his master should straightways know it, and not rest free from importuning until either the fellow had put away his fault or their master his fellow. And to make his mind known in this and all other matters he used very effectual signs, being able therethrough to receive and perform any enjoined errand. Besides, he was assisted with so firm a memory that he would not only know any party whom he had once seen for ever after, but also make him known to any other by some special observation and difference. Upon a brother of his God laid the like infirmity, but did not recompense it with the like rarity.

Somewhat near the place of his birth there dwelt another so affected, or rather defected, whose name was Kempe: which two, when they chanced to meet, would use such kind embracements, such strange, often, and earnest tokenings, and such hearty laughters and other passionate gestures, that their want of a tongue seemed rather an hindrance to others conceiving them than to their conceiving one another.

Gwarnack, in this Hundred, was the Bevils' ancient seat, whose two daughters and heir married Arundel of Trerice and Greinvile.

Wolvedon, alias Golden, fell unto Tregian, by match with the inheritrix thereof. Tregean signifieth the Giants' Town. Their son married in Lanherne house: their grandchild with the Lord Stourton's daughter; he beareth Erm. on a chief S. three martlets O.

It standeth in Probus parish, whose high and fair church tower of hewed moor-stone was builded within compass of our remembrance by the well disposed inhabitants. And here also dwelleth one Williams, a wealthy and charitable farmer, grandfather to sixty persons now living, and able lately to ride twelve miles in a morning for being witness to the christening of a child to whom he was great-great-grandfather.

From hence, drawing towards the south sea, we will touch at the late park of Lanhadron, because there groweth an oak bearing his leaves speckled with white, as doth another called Painter's Oak in the hundred of East. But whether the former partake any supernatural property to foretoken the owner's soon ensuing death when his leaves are all of one colour (as I have heard some report) let those affirm who better know it. Certain it is that divers ancient families in England are admonished by such predictions.

Grampond, if it took that name from any great bridge, hath now *nomen sine re* [the name without the thing], for the bridge there is supported with only a few arches, and the corporation but half replenished with inhabitants, who may better vaunt of their town's antiquity, than the town of their ability.

Of Pentuan I have spoken before. For the present it harboureth Master Dart, who as divers other gentlemen well descended and accommodated in Devon, do yet rather make choice of a pleasing and retired equality in the little Cornish angle. He matched with Roscarrocke.

Penwarne in the same parish of Mevagesy, alias St Mevie and Isy (two nothing ambitious saints in resting satisfied with the partage of so petty a limit) is vested in Master Otwell Hill, as heir to his mother, the daughter and heir to Cosowarth, to whom it likewise accrued by matching with the daughter and heir of that name: a seat, through his fruitfulness and other appurtenances, supplying the owner large means of hospitality, and by him so employed, who reckoneth to receive most good when he doth it. He deriveth himself from a populous and well regarded family in Lancashire, and married the daughter of Denham; and beareth G. a chevron between three garbes Ermine.

At the adjoining Saint Tue [St Ewe] dwelleth Master Richard Tremayn, descended from a younger branch of Colocumb house in Devon, who being learned in the laws is yet to learn, or at least to practise, how he may make other profit thereby, than by hoarding up treasure of gratitude in the mindful breasts of poor and rich on whom he, *gratis*, bestoweth the fruits of his pain and knowledge. He married Coffyn; he beareth G. three arms in circle joined at the trunks O. with hands proper.

Dudman, a well-known foreland to most sailors, here shouldereth out the ocean, to shape the same a large bosom between itself and Rame Head which are wellnear twenty miles in distance. Amongst sundry proverbs allotting an impossible time of performance, the Cornishmen have this one, 'When Rame Head and Dudman meet'. Whose possession, yet not themselves, met in Sir Piers Edgecumb, as enjoying that in right of his wife, and this by descent from his father.

Bodrugan, a large domain adjoining thereunto (which I will not derive from Sir Bors de Ganis, though the neighbours so say) was the dwelling of Sir Henry Trenowith, a man of great livelihood, who changed his name with the house, and lost house and holding through the attainder for rebellion against King Henry VII. The King bestowed it, by an entailed gift, upon Sir Richard Edgecumb.

Next lieth the foreremembered Caryhayes (*Kery haz* in Cornish signifieth, to bear his seed, or as some other define it, delighting in seed) descended to Mr Charles Trevanion, the present possessioner by a long rank of ancestors from Arundel's daughter and heir. His father married the daughter of Morgan, and sister to the first Lord Hunsdon's wife, which brought him an honourable ally. Three of this gentleman's elder brethren forewent him in succession to their father's inheritance, and passed to the better world in a single life: himself by matching the daughter and heir of Witchalse, whose mother was co-heir to Marwood, hath raised issue unto them, and continueth the hope of posterity. Sir William Trevanion, his grandsire, took to wife the said Sir Richard Edgecumb's daughter. The Trevanions' arms are A. a fesse B., charged with three escalops O., between two chevrons G.

Roseland is a circuit containing certain parishes hereabouts, and benefiting the owners with his fruitfulness, so that though the original of his name came (perhaps), as Master Camden noteth, from his former thickets, yet his present estate better resembleth a flowery effect.

By this time we approach the limits of Falmouth Haven, upon one of whose creeks standeth the market and incorporate town of Tregny, not specially memorable (in my knowledge) for any extraordinary worth or accident.

Of better regard is Truro, alias Truru, or Trisow, as the principal town of the haven, privileged with a mayoralty, and benefited with the general western sessions, coinages, markets, fairs, &c. The shape of the town and etymon of the name may be learned out of this Cornish prophetical rhyme:

> *Tru ru,*
> *Triueth eu,*
> *Ombdina geueth try ru.*

Which is to say, 'Truro consisteth of three streets, and it shall in time be said, "Here Truro stood".'

A like mischief of a mystery they observe, that in taking *T* from the town there resteth *ru, ru*, which in English soundeth Woe, woe. But whatsoever shall become thereof hereafter, for the present I hold it to have got the start in wealth of any other Cornish town, and to come behind none in buildings, Launceston only excepted, where there is more use and profit of fair lodgings through the county assizes. I wish that they would likewise deserve praise for getting and employing their riches in some industrious trade to the good of their country, as the harbour's opportunity inviteth them.

Descending from Truro to the haven's mouth by water, you are overlooked by sundry gentlemen's commodious seats, as Fentengollan, in English the Hart's Well, lately appertaining to master Carmynow, by interpretation often loving, and now to Master Holcomb who married the daughter of Master Peter Courtney.

Master Sayer's house Ardevora, inhabited by Mr Thomas Peyton, a gentleman for his age and virtue deserving a regardful estimation; [gap – Tregothnan], Master Bescawn's; [gap], Master Sayer's; but amongst all, upon that side of the river, Talverne, for pleasant prospect, large scope, and other housekeeping commodities, challengeth the pre-eminence. It was given to a younger brother of Lanhearne, for some six or seven descents past, and hath bred gentlemen of good worth and calling, amongst whom I may not forget the late kind and valiant Sir John

Arundell who matched with Godolphin, nor John, his virtuous and hopeful succeeding son, who married with Carew, though this remembrance renew that sorrow which once I partly expressed in the ensuing epitaph:

> Seek not, blind eyes, the living with the dead,
> 'Tis earth you see: our Arundel is gone
> To join with Christ, as member to his head,
> And scorns and pities this our bootless moan.
> > Yet pardon us, sweet soul: man's nature bears
> > We to thy loss should sacrifice our tears.
>
> Thou time hast changed to eternity,
> But timeless was that time in our regard,
> Since nought thou leav'st us save the memory
> Of thy dear worth, so soon not to be spar'd.
> > Soft be the grave unto thy resting bones:
> > Short be the date that us again atones.

Upon the east side of the haven's entrance, Saint Mary's, alias St Mawes Castle, with his point-blank ordnance controlleth any shipping that deserve a denial of admission or passage, and is commanded by Master Vivian, a gentleman, who through his worth deserveth, and with due care and judgment dischargeth, the martial and civil governments committed to his trust.

We will close up this Hundred after our usual manner, with the gentlemen of mark, but not orderly marked. Such are Tanner, who married the daughter of Roscarrock: who beareth A. on a chief S. three morions' heads O. Pomeroy, a branch of Berry Pomeroy in Devon: he beareth O. a lion rampant G. who matched with Tanner, and whose daughter and heir apparent hath taken to husband the young Penkevil, who beareth A. two chevrons, and in a chief a lion passant G.

Polwheele, whose name is deduced from his dwelling and his dwelling may be interpreted, The miry work, linked in wedlock with the co-heir of Trencreeke, in English the town of the Borough. His mother was Lower of Trelask; Polwheel beareth S. a saultier engrayled Erm.

Hearle, lineally descended from sundry knights, who wedded Trevanion: and his son Treffry. He beareth A. a fess G. between three sheldrakes proper. Sawle, who espoused Rashleigh, and his father Kendall, &c and beareth A. a chevron between three falcons' heads erased S.

I must now for a while bid the south sea farewell, until a new opportunity call me to end the other part of Falmouth haven, and take the hundred of Pider in task, which confineth with Powder in situation, as it resembleth the same in denomination. *Pider* in Cornish is Four in English, and this is the fourth hundred of Cornwall if you begin your reckoning from the western part, at Penwith, which (signifying a head) doth seem so to require it.

In entering this hundred Padstowe first presenteth itself, a town and haven of suitable quality, for both (though bad) are the best that the north Cornish coast possesseth. The borough gave name to the harbour, and borroweth it of Petrock and Stowe, contracting the same into Padstowe. It hath lately purchased a corporation, and reapeth greatest thrift by trafficking with Ireland, for which it commodiously lieth. The harbour is barred with banks of sand, made (through uniting their weak forces) sufficiently strong to resist the ocean's threatening billows, which (divorced from their parent) find their rage subdued by the other's lowly submission.

Mr Nicholas Prideaux from his new and stately house thereby taketh a full and large prospect of the town, haven, and country adjoining, to all which his wisdom is a stay, his authority a direction. He married one of Viel's co-heirs; and although endowed with fair revenues in Devon, maketh Cornwall beholden to his residence. He beareth A. a chevron S. in chief a file with three lambeaux G.

The salt water leaving Padstowe floweth up into the country that it may embrace the river Camel, and having performed this natural courtesy, ebbeth away again to yield him the freer passage, by which means they both undergo Wade bridge, the longest, strongest, and fairest that the shire can muster. It took his name of a ford adjoining, which affordeth a way, not so safe as compendious, when the tide is out.

Wade bridge delivereth you into a waste ground where nine long and great stones, called The Sisters, stand in a rank together, and seem to have been so pitched for continuing the memory of somewhat, whose notice is yet envied us by time. Near to Belowdy, commonly and not unproperly termed Beelowzy, the top of a hill is environed with deep treble trenches, which leave a large plain space in the midst; they call it Castell-an-Danis, of which my former book maketh mention, and it seemeth (in times past)

172

to have been a matter of moment, the rather for that a great causeway (now covered with grass) doth lead unto it.

Saint Columbs is a big parish and a mean market town, subject to the lordship and patronage of the Lanhearn Arundels who for many descents lie there interred, as the inscriptions on their gravestones do testify. Their name is derived from *Hirondelle*, in French a swallow, and out of France at the conquest they came, and six swallows they give in arms. The country people entitle them, The Great Arundels, and greatest stroke for love, living, and respect, in the country heretofore they bare. Their said house of Lanhearne standeth in the next parish, called Mawgan. *Ladn* is Cornish for a bank, and on a bank the same is seated; what *herne* may mean ignorance bids me keep silence. It is appurtenanced with a large scope of land, which (while the owners there lived) was employed to frank hospitality; yet the same wanted wood, in lieu whereof they burned heath, and generally it is more regardable for profit than commendable for pleasure. The gentleman now living married Anne, the daughter of Sir Henry Gerningham: his father (a man of goodly presence and kind magnanimity) married the daughter of the Earl of Darby, and widow to the Lord Stourton. He beareth S. six swallows in pile A.

Little Colan hath less worth the observation, unless you will deride or pity their simplicity who sought at our Lady Nant's well there to foreknow what fortune should betide them, which was in this manner. Upon Palm Sunday these idle-headed seekers resorted thither with a palm cross in one hand and an offering in the other: the offering fell to the priest's share, the cross they threw into the well, which, if it swam, the party should outlive that year, if it sank, a short ensuing death was boded, and perhaps not altogether untruly, while a foolish conceit of this halsening might the sooner help it onwards. A contrary practice to the goddess Juno's lake in Laconia: for there, if the wheaten cakes cast in upon her festival day were by the water received, it betokened good luck; if rejected, evil. The like is written by Pausanias of Inus in Greece, and by others touching the offerings thrown into the furnace of Mount Etna in Sicily.

From hence, by the double duty of consanguinity and affinity, I am called to stop at Cosowarth, which inhabitance altered the inhabitants from their former French name, *Escudifer*, in English, Iron-shield, to his own, as they prove by old evidence, not needing in the Norman kings new birth, to be distinguished by the Reigner's number.

Cosowarth, in Cornish, importeth The High Grove, and well stored with trees it hath been, neither is yet altogether destitute.

John, the heir of that house, having by the daughter of Williams issue only one daughter, Catherine, suffered part of his lands to descend unto the children of her first husband, Alen Hill; another part he entailed in her second marriage with Arundel of Trerice, to their issue. The house of Cosowarth and the ancient inheritance there adjoining he gave to the heirs male of his stock, by which conveyance his uncle John succeeded, who married the daughter of Sir William Lock, King Henry VIII's merchant, and by him knighted, for that with equal courage and hazard he took down the Pope's bull set up at Antwerp against his Sovereign. He had issue Thomas, Edward, Michael, John, and Robert. Thomas married the daughter of St Aubyn, on whom he begat John and Dorothy. John the elder and Robert never tasted the sweet and sour of bridal fruit.

Michael took to wife Sidenham's daughter of Dulverton in Somerset, and is father of issue only female. He addicteth himself to an ecclesiastical life, and therein joining poetry with divinity endeavoureth to imitate the holy prophet David, whose Psalms, of his translation into English metre, receive the general applause beyond a great many other well-deserving undertakers of the same task.

John the youngest succeeding in this inheritance, upon just cause, good conscience and grateful kindness, renewed the entail which his father Thomas had cut off, and in a single estate, and the universal love of all that conversed with him, made a short period of his long-hoped life: whose decease I bewailed in these rhymes:

> He that at sea and land amidst his foes,
> By courage guided, sought, and 'scapt his death,
> Lo, here, amongst his friends whom liking chose
> And nature lent, hath up resign'd his breath.
>> Unripened fruit in growth, precious in hope,
>> Rare in effect, had fortune given scope.
> Our eyes with tears perform thine obsequy,
> And hearts with sighs, since hands could yield none aid;
> Our tongues with praise preserve thy memory,
> And thoughts with grief, since we behind are stayed.
>> Coswarth, farewell, death which us parts atwain,
>> Ere long, in life, shall us conjoin again.

His sister married Kendall. Edward, his uncle and heir, by virtue of these entails, married the daughter of Arundel of Trerice, and from a civil courtier's life in his younger years, reposeth his elder age on the good husbandry of the country, having raised posterity sufficient for transplanting the name into many other quarters. He beareth A. on a chevron between three wings B. five bezants.

Against you have passed towards the west somewhat more than a mile, Trerice, anciently Treres, offereth you the view of his costly and commodious buildings. What *Tre* is, you know already, *res* signifieth a rushing of fleeting away, and upon the declining of a hill the house is seated. In Edward III's reign, Ralph Arundel matched with the heir of this land and name, since which time his issue hath there continued, and increased their livelihood by sundry like inheritors, as St John, Iew, Durant, Thurlebear, &c. Precisely to rip up the whole pedigree were more tedious than behooveful: and therefore I will only (as by the way) touch some few points which may serve (in part) to show what place and regard they have borne in the Commonwealth.

There was an indenture made (7 Henry V) between Hugh Courtney, Earl of Devon, Lieutenant to the king, for a sea voyage in defence of the realm: and Sir John Arundel of Trerice, for accompanying him therein.

He was Sheriff of Cornwall, 8 Henry V.

John Earl of Huntingdon, under his seal of arms (5 Henry VI), made Sir John Arundel of Trerice Seneschal of his household, as well in peace as in war, gave him ten pound fee and allowed him entertainment in his house for one gentleman, three yeomen, one boy and six horses.

The same Earl, styling himself Lieutenant-General to John Duke of Bedford, Constable and Admiral of England, wrote (8 Henry VI) to the said Sir John Arundel, then Vice-Admiral of Cornwall, for the release of a ship, which he had arrested by virtue of his office.

The Queen, by her letter (3 Henry VII, 12 October), advertised Sir John Arundel of Trerice Esquire that she was brought in childbed of a prince.

The King wrote (11 Henry VIII) to Sir John Arundel of Trerice that he should give his attendance at Canterbury about the entertainment of the Emperor, whose landing was then and there expected.

John Arundel of Trerice Esquire took prisoner (14 Henry VIII) Duncane Campbell, a Scot, in a fight at sea, as our chronicle mentioneth, concerning which I thought it not amiss to insert a letter sent him from Thomas

Duke of Norfolk (to whom he then belonged) that you may see the style of those days.

By the Duke of Norf.

Right well-beloved, in our hearty wise we commend ourselves unto you, letting you wit, that by your servant, this bearer, we have received your letters dated at Truru the 5. day of this month of April, by which we perceive the goodly, valiant, and icopardous enterprise, it hath pleased God of late to send you, by the taking of Duncane Camel & other Scots on the sea; of which enterprise we have made relation unto the King's Highness, who is not a little joyous and glad to hear of the same, and hath required us instantly in his name, to give you thanks for your said valiant courage and bold enterprise in the premises; and by these our letters for the same your so doing we not only thank you in our most effectual wise, but also promise you, that during our life, we will be glad to advance you to any preferment we can. And over this, you shall understand, our said sovereign lord's pleasure is, that you shall come and repair to his Highness, with diligence in your own person, bringing with you the said captive, and the master of the Scottish ship; at which time you shall not only be sure of his especial thanks by mouth, & to know his further pleasure therein, but also of us to further any your reasonable pursuits unto his Highness, or any other, during our life, to the best of our power, accordingly. Written at Lambeth, the 11. day of April aforesaid.

Superscribed: To our right well-beloved servant, John Arundel of Trerice

The King wrote (35 Henry VIII) to Sir John Arundel of Trerice touching his discharge from the Admiralty of the fleet, lately committed unto him, & that he should deliver the ship which he sailed in to Sir Nic. Poynts.

The same year the King wrote to him again, that he should attend him in his wars against the French king, with his servants, tenants and others, within his rooms and offices, especially horsemen.

Other letters from the King there are, whose date is not expressed, neither can I by any means hunt it out.

One, to his servant, John Arundel of Trerice Esquire, willing him, not to repair with his men, and to wait in the rearward of his army as he had commanded him, but to keep in a readiness for some other service.

Another, to Sir John Arundel of Trerice, paying and desiring him to the Court, the Quindene of St Hilary next, wheresoever the King shall then be within the realm.

There are also letters, directed to Sir John Arundel of Trerice, from the King's Council, by some of which it appeareth (Edward VI) that he was Vice-Admiral of the King's ships in the West Seas, and by others that he had the goods and lands of certain rebels given him, for his good service against them.

The Queen wrote to Sir John Arundel of Trerice (1 Mary) praying and requiring him, that he, with his friends and neighbours, should see the Prince of Spain most honourably entertained, if he fortuned to land in Cornwall.

She wrote to him (2 Mary) being then Sheriff of Cornwall, touching the election of the Knights of the Shire, and the burgesses for the Parliament.

She likewise wrote to him (2 & 3 Philip and Mary) that (notwithstanding the instructions to the justices) he should muster and furnish his servants, tenants and others under his rule and offices, with his friends, for the defence and quieting of the country, withstanding of enemies, and any other employment; as also to certify what force of horse and foot he could arm.

These few notes I have culled out of many others. Sir John Arundell, last mentioned, by his first wife, the co-heir of Bevill, had issue Roger, who died in his father's lifetime; and Katherine, married to Prideaux; Roger by his wife Trendenham left behind him a son, called John. Sir John's second wife was daughter to Erisy and widow to Gourlyn, who bare him John, his succeeder in Trerice and much other fair revenues, whose due commendation, because another might better deliver than myself who touch him as nearly as Tacitus did Agricola, I will therefore bound the same within his desert, and only say this, which all who knew him shall testify with me: that of his enemies he would take no wrong nor on them any revenge, and being once reconciled, embraced them without scruple or remnant of gall. Over his kindred he held a wary and chary care, which bountifully was expressed when occasion so required, reputing himself not only principal of the family but a general father to them all. Private respects ever with him gave place to the common good; as for frank, well ordered, and continual hospitality, he outwent all show of competence; spare but discreet of speech: better conceiving than delivering: equally stout and kind, not upon lightness of humour, but soundness of judgment: inclined to commiseration, ready to relieve. Briefly, so accomplished in virtue, that those who for many years together waited in nearest place about him, and by his example learned to hate untruth, have often deeply protested how no curious observation of theirs could ever descry in him any one notorious vice.

By his first foreremembered wife he had four daughters, married to Carew, Summaster, Cosowarth, and Denham; by his latter, the daughter of Sir Robert Denis, two sons and two daughters. The elder, even from his young years, began where his father left, and with so temperate a course treadeth just in his footsteps, that he inheriteth as well his love as his living. The younger brother followeth the Netherland wars with so well-liked a carriage that he outgoeth his age and time of service in preferment. The mother equalleth her husband's former children, and generally all his kindred, in kind usage, with her own, and is by them all again so acknowledged and respected.

Of St Peran we have spoken before, which too well brooketh his surname, *in Sabulo* [in the sand]: for the light sand carried up by the north wind from the seashore daily continueth his covering and marring the land adjoinant, so as the distress of this deluge drave the inhabitants to remove their church. Howbeit, when it meeteth with any crossing brook, the same (by a secret antipathy) restraineth and barreth his farther encroaching that way.

In Withiel parish of this hundred, one Gidly, not many years sithence, digged down a little hillock or barrow called Borsneevas, in English, Cheapful, therewith to thicken his other ground; in the bottom of which he found three white stones, trianglewise (as pillars) supporting another flat one, some two feet and a half square, and in the midst between them, and under it, an earthen pot, half full of a black slime and ill-savouring substance, which (doubtless) was once the ashes of some notable person, there committed to that manner of burial.

Saint Agnes, one of the high hills which I specially recited in my former book, by his entrails (like Prometheus) feedeth the tinners' pecking or picking bills with a long-lived profit, albeit their scarce eagle eyes sometimes mistake the shadow for the substance, and so offer up degenerate tears as a late sacrifice to repentance. The neighbours have observed that of two lakes near adjoining to this hill, and so each to other, the one will foster fish and the other none at all.

Neither may I omit new Kaye, a place in the north coast of this hundred, so called because in former times the neighbours attempted to supply the defect of nature by art, in making there a kay [quay] for the road of shipping; which conceit they still retain, though want of means in themselves or the place have left the effect *in nubibus* [in the clouds, 'up in the air'], and only lent them the benefit of lestercocks and fisherboats.

I cannot finish this Hundred with the relation of many more gentlemen, either through want of them, or in myself. Trenance added to his own livelihood the possessions of Littleton, to whom, as sister's son and general heir, he succeeded: he married Kendall, and his son Roscarrocke; he beareth A. a fesse between three swords S.

There dwelleth also Master Tredenick, who matched with the daughter of Vivian, and his father, of Marow, who beareth O. on a bend S. three bucks' heads cabased A. As also Langherne B. a chevron between three escalops O. Burlace, A. on a bend S. two hands tearing in sunder a horse-shoe of the field; and others.

Kerier Hundred

Kery, in Cornish, signifieth bearing, and yet you must bear with me if I forbear to derive Kerier herefrom until I see some reason for my warrant, wherefore leaving that, I will weave on my former web of Falmouth Haven. And first, a word or two touching the same in general, ere I descend to the yet undescribed west side in particular.

The river Fala, falling here into the sea's wide-gaping mouth, hath endowed it with that name.

In the very entrance of the harbour lieth a rock, rather disgracing than endamaging the same, for with the ebb it is discovered, and at the flood marked by a pole purposely fixed thereupon. For the rest, such as compare Plymmouth and Falmouth together observe that Plymmouth creeks are mostly coasted with plain shores, Falmouth with steep, which maketh that the more delightful for prospect, this the more safe for riding. Again, they say that Falmouth lieth farther out in the trade way, and so offereth a sooner opportunity to wind-driven shipping than Plymmouth, but that Plymmouth hath a better outlet from his Catwater for sailors bound to the westwards, and from Hamoaze for those that would fare to the east, than Falmouth. Likewise, as Plymmouth vaunteth richer and fairer towns and greater plenty of fish than Falmouth, so Falmouth braggeth that a hundred sail may anchor within his circuit, and no one of them see the other's top, which Plymmouth cannot equal. Howsoever they agree for competence among themselves, the worst of them by most men's judgments hath the precedence (Milford only excepted) of all other havens in England. And thus much of the whole. Now to the parts.

On the west side, at the very coming in, there riseth a hill called Pendenis, where King Henry VIII, when he took order for fortifying the sea coasts, caused a castle to be builded, with allowance of a petty garrison and some small store of ordnance. Another, somewhat like thereto in plot, but different in site, was then erected on the other side, at St Mawes, of which I have spoken heretofore. Saint Mawes lieth lower and better to annoy shipping, but Pendennis standeth higher and stronger to defend itself. It should seem the fortifier made his advantage of the commodity afforded by the ground, and shot rather at a safe preserving the harbour from sudden attempts of little fleets, and the mastering of pirates, than to withstand any great navy or main invasion.

But her Majesty casting an equal eye to both, or rather a sharper sight to this latter, as quickened through the enemy's divers pretences against these places (whereof Falmouth by miracle, not providence, escaped one) raised a new fort with a garrison upon the Hawe at Plymmouth, and at her great charges, with some little help of the country, added an increase of fortification and soldiers to Pendenis. Howbeit, his greatest strength consisteth in Sir Nicholas Parker, the governor, who demeaning himself no less kindly and frankly towards his neighbours, for the present, than he did resolutely and valiantly, against the enemy when he followed the wars; therethrough commandeth, not only their bodies, by his authority, but also their hearts, by his love, to live and die in his assistance, for their common preservation, and her Highness' service: he beareth B. frettie, and A. a fesse O.

After the declining hill hath delivered you down from this castle, Arwenacke entertaineth you with a pleasing view, for the same standeth so far within the haven's mouth that it is protected from the sea storms, and yet so near thereunto as it yieldeth a ready passage out, besides, the cliff on which the house abutteth is steep enough to shoulder off the waves, and the ground about it plain and large enough for use and recreation. It is owned by Master John Killigrew, who married the daughter of Monck, and heir to her mother [gap in text] and was son to Sir John Killigrew, who matched with Wolverstone: the stock is ancient, and divers of the branches (as I have elsewhere remembered) grown to great advancement in calling and livelihood, by their greater desert: their arms are A. an eagle with two heads displayed within a bordure bezanty S.

Somewhat above Arwennack, Trefuses Point divideth the harbour and yieldeth a several anchoring place on each side thereof, the one called Carrack Road, and the other King's Road. This promontory is possessed and inhabited by a gentleman of that name who suitably to his name, giveth three fusils for his coat, in this sort: A. a chevron between three fusils S. He married the co-heir of Gaurigan, and Mr William Godolphin, late younger brother to Sir Frauncis, her other sister.

Upon the left hand from hence, at the top of a creek, Perin town hath taken up his seat, rather passable than notable for wealth, buildings, and inhabitants, in all which, though near the haven's mouth, it giveth Truro the pre-eminence: the like whereof I observe touching divers other towns of the same situation in Devon, as Salcombe and Kingsbridge, Dartmouth and Totnes, Topsham and Excester: amongst which, those that stand highest up in the country afford therethrough a fitter opportunity of access from all quarters, and so a speedier and larger vent of their commodities.

In Perin was Glasney College, founded by Walter Brounscomb and benefited by John Graundson, Bishops of Excester, which see possesseth fair revenues thereabouts.

Upon another creek on the same side, Carclew hath (after the Cornish manner) well-near metamorphosed the name of Master Bonithon, his owner, into his own. He married the daughter of Vivian, his father of Killigrew, his grandfather of Erisy, and beareth A. a chevron between three fleurs de luce S.

With any memorable act or accident concerning this haven, I cannot acquaint you, save only, that Philip, Archduke of Austriche, during his voyage from Netherland towards Spain (his wife's kingdom) was weather-driven into Weymouth, and, with a kind constraint, received a more royal than welcome entertainment at the hands of King Henry VII, from which he could not free himself, but by redeeming his liberty with De la Pool's captivity. This accomplished, he made choice to take ship again at Falmouth, that so by the shortest cut he might leave least power in fortune, to thwart him any second encumbrance.

Hailford, so called of the fordable river Haill, if elsewhere placed, would carry the reputation of a good harbour, but as it now standeth,

Falmouth's overnear neighbourhood lesseneth his use and darkeneth his reputation, as quitting it only to the worst sort of seafarers, I mean pirates, whose guilty breasts, with an eye in their backs, look warily how they may go out ere they will adventure to enter; and this at unfortified Hailford cannot be controlled, in which regard it not unproperly brooketh his more common term of Helford, and the nickname of Stealfoord.

His shores afford commodious seats to the dwellings of Reskimer, who married St Abin, and beareth B. three bars A. in chief, a wolf passant of the first; and Tregose, who matched with Kendal: his son with Erisy, and beareth B. two bars gemewes in chief a lion passant O., armed and langued G.

And if your ears be not already cloyed with relations of wonders, I will let you understand how I was once carried to see one hereabouts. It is (forsooth) a great rock lying upon the ground, his top deepened to a hollowness, not much unlike in fashion, but far exceeding in proportion, the long half of an egg. This (they say) holdeth water which ebbeth and floweth as the sea, and indeed when I came thither the tide was half out and the pit half empty. By it there stands a chapel and to it there belonged a cover, so as the same seemed in former times to carry some regard. But I have heard credible persons so discredit this wonder that I dare not offer it you as probable, much less thrust it upon you as approved. The name thereof is Hanterdavis, which (turning *d* to *t*) signifieth half a tongue.

More certain, though less wonderful, and yet for the strangeness well worth the viewing, is Mainamber: *Mayne* is a rock, *amber* as some say signifieth Ambrose. And a great rock the same is, advanced upon some others of a meaner size with so equal a counterpoise that the push of a finger will sensibly move it to and fro, but farther to remove it the united forces of many shoulders are over-weak. Wherefore the Cornish wonder-gatherer thus describeth the same:

Be thou thy mother nature's work,
  Or proof of giant's might:
Worthless and ragged though thou show,
  Yet art thou worth the sight.
This hugy rock, one finger's force
  Apparently will move,
But to remove it, many strengths
  Shall all like feeble prove.

Helston, in Cornish *Hellaz*, in English the Green Hall, is a well seated and peopled town, privileged, *secundum usum* [by custom] with the rest, and one of the four coinage places. Under it runneth the river Lo, whose passage into the sea is thwarted by a sand bank, which forceth the same to quurt back a great way and so to make a pool of some miles in compass. It breedeth a peculiar kind of bastard trout, in bigness and goodness exceeding such as live in the fresh water, but cometh short of those that frequent the salt.

The foreremembered bank serveth as a bridge to deliver wayfarers with a compendious passage to the other side, howbeit sometimes with more haste than good speed, for now and then it is so pressed on the inside with the increasing river's weight, and a portion of the utter sand so washed down by the waves, that at a sudden outbreaketh the upper part of the pool, and away goeth a great deal of the sand, water, and fish, which instant, if it take any passenger tardy, shrewdly endangereth him to flit for company, and some have so miscarried.

To this pool adjoineth Mr Penrose's house, whose kind entertainment hath given me, and many others, experience of these matters. He married a daughter of Rashleigh: he beareth A. three bends S. charged with nine rests of the field.

Those two rivers of Haill and Lo, rising not far asunder, do enclose between them as they run into the sea a neck of land particularised with the name of Meneag, and in regard of his fruitfulness not unworthy of a severance.

Within this circuit lie Trelawarren, Mr Vivian's house, and Erisy, seated in two parishes, and descended by a long rank of ancestors to the gentleman of that name, now in ward. His father married Carew: his grandsire one of the Militons' co-heirs, who overliving her husband, ended the course of her long and well commended widowhood in becoming lady to Sir Nicholas Parker. The Erisies bear S. a chevron between three griffons sergreant O.

Clowance (derived from *Cloow*, which signifieth to hear) is the possession and dwelling of Mr Saintabin, whose very name (besides the conquest roll) deduceth his first ancestors out of France. His grandfather married Greinvile: his father one of Whittington's co-heirs: which later couple, in a long and peaceable date of years, exercised a kind, liberal and never discontinued hospitality. Himself took to wife the daughter of

Mallet, and with ripe knowledge and sound judgement dischargeth the place which he beareth in his country. He beareth O. on a cross G. five bezants.

Pengueraz in Cornish importeth a head to help; from which, some deduce the etymon of Pengersick, a fair house in an unfruitful soil, sometimes the inhabitance of Mr Militon, Captain of the Mount and husband to Godolphin, whose son being lost in his travel beyond the seas, enriched six distaffs with his inheritance. They were bestowed in marriage (but by me not orderly marshalled) as followeth: 1. to Erisy and Sir Nicholas Parker; 2. to Lanine; 3. to Trefuses and Tregodeck; 4. to Trenwith, Arundel and Hearle; 5. to Bonithon; 6. to Abbot.

Not far from thence riseth Godolghan ball, or hill, at whose foot standeth a house of the same name and so intitling his owner, though lately declined (with a milder accent) to Godolphin; in Cornish it signifieth a white eagle, and such arms they carry in this sort: G. an eagle displayed with two heads, between three flowers de luce A.

This hill hath for divers descents supplied those gentlemen's bountiful minds with large means accruing from their tin-works, and is now possessed by Sir Frauncis Godolphin, Knight, whose zeal in religion, uprightness in justice, providence in government, and plentiful housekeeping, have won him a very great and reverent reputation in his country, and these virtues, together with his services to her Majesty, are so sufficiently known to those of highest place as my testimony can add little light thereunto; but by his labours and inventions in tin matters, not only the whole country hath felt a general benefit, so as the several owners have thereby gotten very great profit out of such refuse works as they before had given over for unprofitable, but her Majesty hath also received increase of her customs by the same at least to the value of £10,000. Moreover, in those works which are of his own particular inheritance, he continually keepeth at work three hundred persons or thereabouts, and the yearly benefit that out of those his works accrueth to her Majesty amounteth, *communibus annis* [taking one year with another], to £1000 at the least, and sometimes to much more; a matter very remorceable, and perchance not to be matched again by any of his condition in the whole realm. He succeeded to the inheritance of his uncle, Sir William Godolphin, who, as hath been said before, demeaned himself very valiantly in a charge which he bare at Boulogne towards the latter end of the reign of King Henry VIII, and is like to leave the same to another Sir William, his son, who giveth hope, not only of the sustaining, but increasing the reputation of his family. He matched with Killigrew, his father with Bonython, his grandfather with Glynne.

Divers other gentlemen there dwell in this hundred, as Lanyne, the husband of Kekewitch, his father married Militon, and beareth S. a castle, A., standing in waves B. over the same a falcon hovering with bells O. Penwarne, that matched with the co-heir of Trencreek, who beareth S. a chevron between three flowers de luce A. Lagherne, who took to wife the daughter of Nants, and beareth B. a chevron between three escalops O. Nansperyan couple in matrimony with [gap in text] and his two daughters and heirs apparent, with Prideaux, and Matthew: who beareth A. three lozenges S.

Penwith Hundred

My last labour, for closing up this wearisome Survey, is bounded, as Cornwall itself, and so the west part of England, with Penwith Hundred. The name in English signifieth the Head of Ashen Trees, belike for some such eminent mark while the country was better stored with timber. The Danes sailing about Penwith Steort (saith Hoveden) made foul havoc in Devon and Cornwall.

Upon the north sea lieth Nants, which importeth a valley, and houseth a gentleman who therethrough hath worn out his former name of Trengove, in English the smith's town, and assumed this; he married Sir John Arundel's daughter of Trerice, and beareth A. a cross hawmed S. During summer season the seals haunt a cave in the cliff thereby, and you shall see great store of them apparently show themselves, and approach very near the shore at the sound of any loud music or other such noise.

Beyond Nants, Mr Basset possesseth Tehiddy, who married Godolphin, his father Coffyn: he beareth O. three piles in point G., a canton Er. with a difference.

And so, leaving these private inhabitances and keeping still the north coast, we arrive at the town and port of St Ies, both of mean plight, yet with their best means (and often, to good and necessary purpose) succouring distressed shipping. Order hath been taken, and attempts made for bettering the road with a pier, but either want, or slackness, or impossibility, hitherto withhold the effect. The whiles, plenty of fish is here taken, and sold very cheap.

As you row to the westward from hence, the sea floweth into a large cave farther up than any man durst yet adventure to discover, and the cliffs thereabouts muster long streaks of a glittering hue, which import a show of copper; and copper mines are found, and wrought in the grounds adjoining.

Mr Camden observeth that near hereunto stood the watch-tower mentioned by Orosius, and oppositely placed to such another in Galicia.

Stepping over to the south sea (for the distance is in comparison but a step) St Michael's Mount looketh so aloft as it brooketh no concurrent for the highest place. Ptolemy termeth it *Ocrinum*, the Cornishmen, *Cara Cowz in Clowze*, that is, the Hoar Rock in the Wood. The same is sundered from the mainland by a sandy plain of a flight-shoot in breadth, passable at the ebb on foot, with boat on the flood. Your arrival on the farther side is entertained by an open green of some largeness, which finishing where the hill beginneth, leaves you to the conduction of a winding and craggy path, and that at the top delivereth you into a little plain occupied for the greatest part by a fort of the old making. It compriseth lodgings for the captain and his garrison, and a chapel for devotion, this latter built by William Earl of Morton, to whom William the Conqueror his uncle gave much lands in those quarters, and greatly haunted, while folk endured their merits, by far travelling. They have a tye-pit [collecting rainwater], not so much satisfying use as relieving necessity. A little without the castle there is a bad seat in a craggy place, called St Michael's Chair, somewhat dangerous for access and therefore holy for the adventure.

Until Richard I's reign the Mount seemeth to have served only for religion, and (during his imprisonment) to have been first fortified by Henry de Pomeray, who surprised it and expulsed the monks. Howbeit soon after, when he became ascertained of his Sovereign's enlargement, the very fear of ensuing harm wrought in him a present effect of the uttermost that any harm could bring, namely his death: whereon the old cell and new fort were surrendered to the Archbishop of Canterbury in the King's behalf. Thus Hoveden reporteth.

But the descendants from this Pomeray make a somewhat different relation of this accident; for they affirm that a sergeant at arms of the King's came to their ancestor at his castle of Berry Pomeroy in Devon, received kind entertainment for certain days together, and at his departure was gratified with a liberal reward, in counterchange whereof he then, and no sooner, revealing his long concealed errand, flatly arresteth his host to make his immediate appearance before the King for answering a capital crime. Which unexpected and ill-carried message the gentleman took in such despite as with his dagger he stabbed the messenger to the heart; and then well knowing in so superlative an offence all hope of pardon foreclosed, gets to a sister of his abiding in this Mount, bequeatheth a large portion of his land to the religious people there for redeeming his soul, and lastly causeth himself to be let blood unto death, for leaving the remainder to his heir; from which time forward this place continued rather a School of Mars than the Temple of Peace. For shortly after the discomfiture of Henry VI's party by Edward IV at Barnet Field, John Earl of Oxford, who had made one, and one of the principal on the weaker side, arrived here by shipping, disguised himself with some of his followers in pilgrim's habits, therethrough got entrance, mastered the garrison, and seized the place. Which thus politically won he as valiantly kept, and kept a long time defended against the King's power, until reasonable conditions swayed him to a surrender.

A like surprise, but of later date, I read in Popelinière, touching the like named and seated mount in Normandy.

During the last Cornish commotion, divers gentlemen with their wives and families fled to the protection of this place, where the rebels besieged them, first winning the plain at the hill's foot by assault when the water was out, and then the even ground on the top by carrying up great trusses of hay before them, to blench the defendants' sight and deaden their shot. After which they could make but slender resistance, for no sooner should any one within peep out his head over those enflanked walls but he became an open mark to a whole shower of arrows. This disadvantage, together with the women's dismay and decrease of victuals, forced a surrender to those rakehells' mercy, who, nothing guilty of that effeminate virtue, spoiled their goods, imprisoned their bodies, and were rather by God's gracious providence than any want of will, purpose, or attempt, restrained from murdering the principal persons.

Here also was the Lady Katherine Gordon (an unfit yoke-fellow for that counterfeit Prince, Perkin Warbeck) taken by the Lord Daubney for the King. Of this, as the last wonder:

> Who knows not Mighel's Mount and Chair,
> The pilgrims' holy vaunt?

Both land and island twice a day,
 Both fort and port of haunt.

Under the Mount extendeth a bay for lesser vessels to lie at, and between it and the western shore there is an indifferent good road for shipping, saving upon some winds, called the Mount's Bay: where, by Froissart's report, Sir Robert Knolles landed, what time his return out of France, was by King Edward III commanded, and for his valiant exploits there achieved, very graciously welcomed.

Over against the Mount fronteth a town of petty fortune, pertinently named Marcaiew, or *Marhas Diow*, in English the Thursday's Market, for then it useth this traffic. At the beginning of King Henry VIII's reign it felt the Frenchmen's fiery indignation, who landed there with thirty sail. But the smoke of those poor houses calling in the country to the rescue, made the place over hot for the enemy's any longer abode.

Mousehole in Cornish is name *Portennis*, and in Latin *Portus Insulae*, both importing one sense, to wit, the Island Haven, and so called through a little island placed before it.

Mr Holinshed telleth us that near hereunto, not many years sithence, certain tinners as they were working found spear-heads, battle-axes, and swords of copper, wrapped in linen clouts and little impaired through their long lying.

Pensans, by interpretation the Saint's Head, is a market town not so regardable for his substance as memorable for his late accident of the Spaniards' firing, which fell out in this manner:

The 23rd of July, 1595, soon after the sun was risen and had chased a fog which before kept the sea out of sight, four galleys of the enemy presented themselves upon the coast over-against Mousehole, and there in a fair bay landed about two hundred men, pikes and shot, who forthwith sent their forlorn hope, consisting of their basest people, unto the straggled houses of the country about half a mile compass or more, by whom were burned not only the houses they went by but also the parish church of Paul, the force of the fire being such as it utterly ruined all the great stone pillars thereof. Others of them in that time burned that fisher town Mowsehole, the rest marched as a guard for defence of these firers.

The inhabitants being feared with the Spaniards' landing and burning, fled from their dwellings, and very meanly weaponed met with Sir Francis Godolphin on a green on the west side of Pensance, who that forenoon coming from his house for pacifying some controversies in those western parts, and from the hills espying the fires in that town, church, and houses, hastened thither: who forthwith sent to all the captains of those parts for their speedy repair with their companies, and also sent by post to Sir Francis Drake and Sir John Hawkins (then at Plymmouth with a fleet bound for the Indies) advertisement of the arrival of these four galleys and of their burnings, advising them to look to themselves if there were any greater fleet of the enemy's at sea, and to send west with all haste what succours by sea or land they could spare. Then Sir Francis Godolphin advised that weak assembly to retire into Pensance and to prepare it for defence until the coming of the country forces that he had sent for. But they finding themselves in number something above a hundred, wherein were about thirty or forty shot, though scarce one third of them were serviceable, insisted to march against the enemies to repel them from farther spoils of their houses.

But while they were marching towards them, the Spaniards returned aboard their galleys and presently removed them farther into the bay, where they anchored again, before and near a lesser fisher town called Newlyn. There again with all speed they landed, and embattled in the slope of a hill about four hundred pikes and shot, sending about two ranks of soldiers, three in a rank, up to the top of the hill to discover what forces or ambushes of the country might lie in view: who espying none but those that were returned with Sir Frauncis Godolphin from their forementioned fruitless march, gave notice thereof to their embattled company, whereupon they forthwith marched towards Penzance.

Upon their moving Sir Frauncis Godolphin moved also to enter Penzance before them, and as soon as that weak number were entered into the open green, being of three quarters of a mile length, the galleys ceased not to ply them all that way with their ordnance from their prows as busily as they could. Of which shot, though none were hurt, but only a constable unhorsed without any harm, saving the show on his doublet of the bullets sliding by his back, yet many in a fearful manner, some fell flat to the ground and others ran away.

Sir Frauncis sent after those that were entered Penzance before him, that they should make their stand at the market-place, himself staying hindmost to observe the enemy's order and which way they would make their approach. Which done, he found at the said marketplace but only two resolute shot [musketeers] who stood at his command, and some ten or twelve others that followed him, most of them his own servants; the rest, surprised with fear, fled, whom neither with his persuasions nor threatening with his rapier drawn he could recall.

Finding himself thus abandoned and the enemy entered the town in three parts, he was then forced to depart, the enemies beginning their fire some houses behind him. The town thus fired, as also the forementioned little fisher town Newlyn, they returned again to their galleys.

By this time, towards the evening, the Cornish forces, increased in number and amended in heart, encamped themselves on the green near to the town of Markasew and St Michael's Mount for the defence thereof, and there spent out the night. The next day the enemy made show to land again on the west side of the bay, but seeing the people, though few in number yet resolute to resist, they desisted from their enterprise, and besides, finding themselves annoyed by the shooting of bullets and arrows into their galleys where they rode at anchor, they were forced to remove them farther off.

Soon after, viz. on the 25th of July in the morning, came thither Sir Nic. Clifford, Sir H. Power, and certain other captains who were sent by the generals from Plymmouth to the camp, as some of her Majesty's ships were also sent, who being come as far as the Lizard Head, and those captains to the camp, matters there go on in provident and orderly sort. A plot is laid for intercepting the enemy by ambush if he thrust on shore again, whereto necessity must soon have pressed him for renewing his consumed store of fresh water, but within one hour after the arrival of these captains, the wind, which was until then strong at south-east with mist and rain to have impeached the galleys' return, suddenly changed into the north-west with very fair and clear weather, as if God had a purpose to preserve these his rods for a longer time. The wind no sooner came good, but away pack the galleys with all the haste they could.

Thus have you a summary report of the Spaniards' glorious enterprise and the Cornishmen's infamous cowardice, which (were there any cause) I could qualify by many reasons: as, the suddenness of the attempt, the narrowness of the country, the openness of the town, the advantage of the galleys' ordnance on a people unprepared against such accidents through our long continued peace, and at that very time for the most part either in their tin-works or at sea, who ere the next day made resistance even with a handful, and entered a vowed resolution to revenge their loss at the next encounter if the enemy had landed again.

So might I likewise say, that all these circumstances meeting in any other quarter of the realm would hardly have produced much better effects. But I will not seek to thrust my countrymen into any other folks' company, for shifting them out of sight.

Verily such sudden surprises work more indignity than damage, and more damage than disgrace, and have so been ever construed. Moscow, a head city in a populous dominion, was burned by the roguing Tartars, *anno Domini* 1572; the Capitol, a head fortress in a populous city, was taken by slaves and outlaws, *anno urbis* 292; and yet, who therefore exalteth the Tartars' valiancy above the Muscovite, or the Romans' slaves and outlaws above their masters? Besides, such nap-taking assaults, spoilings, and firings, have in our forefathers' days, between us and France been very common; and yet who is so witless as to twit either or both for the same?

But least hold can the author and actor of this tragedy take to build any vaunt thereon; for oftentimes small troops of ours against far greater forces of theirs, yea (sometimes) after forewarning and preparing, have won, possessed, ransacked, singed, captived, and carried away the towns, wealth, and inhabitants, not only of their Indies but of Portugal and Spain itself. Which Nombre de Dios, St Domingo, Cartagena, the lower town of the Groigne, Penecha, the suburbs of Lisbon, and Cales [Cadiz] will testify beyond all exception. But our countrymen, leaving reason and example, excused themselves by destiny. *In fatis*, they say (and not *in fatuis*) [by fate, not folly] it was that the Cornish people should undergo this misfortune, for an ancient prophecy in their own language hath long run amongst them, how there should land upon the rock of Merlin those that would burn Paul's church, Penzance, and Newlyn. And indeed so is the rock called where the enemy first stept on shore. The prophecy is this:

> *Ewra teyre a war meane Merlyn*
> *Ara lesky Pawle Pensanz ha Newlyn.*

Not far from the land's end there is a little village called Trebegean, in English the Town of the Giant's Grave, near whereunto and within memory (as I have been informed) certain workmen searching for tin discovered a long square vault which contained the bones of an excessive big carcase, and verified this etymology of the name.

At Saint Burien's, a parish of great circuit, and like benefit to the incumbent, King Athelstan accomplished his vow in founding a college of priests, what time he had conquered the Scillane Islands.

Chivarton signifieth a house on the green lea, and a castle on a green hill is given by the gentleman of that name, who, in a quiet single life, maketh no farther use of his knowledge gotten in the laws during his younger age, or that experience wherewith a long course of years hath sithence enriched him, than may tend, *sine lucro* [without profit], to the advancement of public justice, or, *sine strepitu* [without fuss], to the advisement of his private acquaintance. He beareth A. a castle S. standing on a hill V.

Sundry other gentlemen people that remote quarter, as Lavelis, &c. touching whom I must plead, *non sum informatus* [I am uninformed].

Diogenes, after he had tired his scholars with a long Lecture, finding at
last the void paper, 'Be glad, my friends (quoth he) we are come to
harbour.' With the like comfort, in an unlike resemblance, I will
refresh you, who have vouchsafed to travel in the rugged and
wearisome path of mine ill-pleasing style, that now your
journey endeth with the land; to whose Promontory
(by Pomp. Mela, called *Bolerium*: by
Diodorus, *Velerium*: by Volaterane,
Helenium: by the Cornish, *Pedn*
an Laaz: and by the English,
The land's end) because
we are arrived, I will
here sit me down
and rest.

Deo gloria: mihi gratia. 1602. April 23

Index

In this index you will find entries under the modern word rather than the word Carew used – for example 'ports' when he refers to 'havens' – and to the general activity, for example all agricultural matters come under 'agriculture', rather than under 'dressing the soil' or dairying. Various generations of a family are indexed under a single entry, e.g. 'Arundell family' and with just one spelling. Place names are given in the modern spelling. We hope this will make the index easier to use.

Achym family 158
adit 24
Æthelred, King of Wessex 92, 109
agriculture 16-17, 34-6, 39-40, 77-8
Alpsius, Duke of Cornwall 92, 136
Altarnun 146
antiquities 20, 153-4, 163-4, 172-3, 178, 188, 191-2
Antony 116
l'Archdeacon, Sir John 116
archery 85-6
Armada 100-1, 135
Arscot family 139
Arthur, King 72, 99, 143-4, 145
Arundell family 7, 69, 71, 72, 86, 99, 111, 117, 137, 139, 140, 159, 170-1, 173, 174, 175-8, 184, 185
Arwennack 180-1
assizes 108, 137
Athelstan 13, 109, 192
Atwell, Mr (parson/physician) 70-1

barnacles becoming birds 55
Barret family 151
Basset family 185
Bastard family 105
beacons 102
Bevil family 100, 155-6, 164, 167, 177
birds 41-2, 53-6
bishopric 96-8, 127
Blackdon, Leonard 99
Blederic, Duke of Cornwall 92
Bligh family 105, 138

Boconnoc 39, 74
Bodinnick 159
Bodmin 60, 61, 76, 79,, 96, 97, 104, 106, 108, 146-151
Bonaventure, Thomasine 141
Bodrugan 169
Bokelly family 62, 151
Bone, Edward 167
Bonville, Lord 74
Bonython 62, 181, 184
Boscastle 60, 74, 142
Bossiney 108
Bray, John 73
Bray, Lord 74
bridges 60, 69, 81, 152
Brittany [Armorica, Little Britain] and Bretons 18, 77-8, 89, 91, 92, 101, 109, 134, 156
Brondescombe, Bishop 181
Brooke, Lord 74
Brutus the Trojan 11-13, 66, 91
Bude 140
building materials 17-18
building techniques 59-60
Buller family 127, 130, 133, 157, 158
Burlace (Borlase?) family 179

Cador, Duke of Cornwall 92
Caerhays 39, 55, 169
Callington 61, 74, 104, 108
Camden, William 6, 9, 62, 66, 93, 97, 98, 99, 141, 143, 145, 169, 186
Camel, River 172

Camelford 60, 61, 104, 108, 145
Caradoc, Duke of Cornwall 92
Carclew family 62, 181
Cardinham 74
Carew family 69, 71, 116-20, 171, 178, 183
Carew, Richard [the author] 6-7, 99-100, 131
Cargreen 133
Carminow family 62, 118
Carnsew, William 31, 62, 99, 151
Castle-an-Dinas 102, 172-3
castles 95, 101-2, 130-1, 165, 171, 180
cattle 39-40
Cavell family 151
Cavendish, Thomas 135
Cawsand 112-3
Chamond family 39, 106, 139
Champernowne family 116, 124, 127
Cheesewring 154
Chiverton 62, 69, 106, 138, 192
chough, Cornish 56
Chudleigh family 118
church ales 80-4
church house 80
Clifford, Sir Nicholas 190
climate 16
Clyes, Rawe [Ralph] 70
Coad family 158
coal, imported 18, 36
cobblestones 17-18
Coffin family 169, 185
coinage 25, 27
collegiate churches 97, 192
Condor, Earl of Cornwall 93
copper 18, 186
Cordelia 91
Corineus 11, 12, 89, 91
Corington family 39, 137-8
Cornish dialect 64-5

Cornish language 7, 63-4
Cornwall,
    government 90 et seq.
    health and longevity 74
    history of 91-4, 109-112
    landscape 16-17
    mineral extraction 17-33
    origin of name 11
    population 65-6
    trade routes 13-14, 18
Cosowarth [Cosworth] family 62, 118, 168, 173-5, 178
Cotehele 134
Courtenay family 69, 106, 110-11, 117, 128, 138, 140, 166-7
courts 106-8
Crafthole 126
Cranach, Burchard 155
Crantock 97
Cuddenbeak 128

Dartmouth 162, 181
Daunye family 126
Davys, John 135
deer 38-9
Denham family 74, 168, 178
Denny family 118
Devon 12, 13, 26, 34, 39, 41, 43-4, 61, 65, 89, 92, 185
'diamonds' 18, 136
Dimmock family 133
Diodorus Siculus 23, 67
Dodman 169
Doniert [Dungarth], King 92
Doniert's Stone 153-4
Dosmary Pool 144-5
Drake, Sir Francis 132, 135, 189
drift fishing 51
Duchy of Cornwall 94-6
Dungarth, see Doniert

Durant family 175
Durnford family 112, 115

Earldom of Cornwall 93
East Hundred 103-4, 112-138
Edgcumbe family 71, 99, 112-5, 134, 169
Edmund Earl of Cornwall 30
Edward I 31
Edward the Black Prince 94, 134
eels 50
Egbert, King of Wessex 109
Elizabeth, Queen 6, 14, 100-101, 120
English, hostility towards 64, 78
Erisey family 177, 181, 183, 184
Exeter 13, 110, 111, 181

fairs 60-1
falconry 41, 84
Falmouth Haven 43, 170, 179-80, 181
farmers 77-8
feasts 80-4
fish, freshwater 43, 45-8
  saltwater 45-54
fishing 45-54, 76
fishponds 120-5, 164
Fitz family 130, 151
Fitzwilliams family 158
Flamank family 111, 151
folklore and customs, examples of
  21, 37, 42, 44, 50, 55, 126, 144, 146, 150, 164, 166, 182
  see also 'portents'
Fortescue family 128
Fountain family 130
Fowey 43, 60, 105, 158-163
foxes 38
friaries 97
Frobisher, Sir Martin 135
fruit growing 36

fuels 36

gaol see prisons
Gaveston, Piers 94
gentlemen 74-6, 78
Geoffrey of Cornwall 68
Gerningham, Sir Henry 173
Gilbert, Sir Humphrey 135
Gille, Nicholas 92
Glasney College 181
Glyn family 185
Godfrey of Cornwall 68
Godolphin family 62, 72, 99-100, 102, 127, 171, 181, 184-5, 188-90
Gogmagog 11, 12
Goit, John 90
Golant 161
gold 18
Golsithney 61
Goneril, Duchess of Cornwall 91
Gorlois, Duke of Cornwall 92
Gourlyn family 177
Grampound 60, 104, 168
Grandisson, Bishop 181
Grenville family 14, 72-3, 99-100, 131, 135, 137, 139, 183
gwary [miracle plays] 84

Halgaver 150
Hall Walk 158-9
Halton 133
harvest dinners 80
Harris family 99, 157-8
Hatch family 118
Hawkins, Sir John 135, 189
Hearle family 171
Hechins (Hutchings?) family 131
Helford 43, 181-2
Helston 27, 60, 76, 97, 104, 108, 183
Hender family 73, 74

Hensbarrow 166
Henry VII 31, 112, 147
Henry VIII 95, 135
Herstane, Bishop of Cornwall 96
Hill family 99, 106, 133, 134, 168, 174
Hingston Down 135-6
Holcombe family 170
holidays 22-3
Holinshed, Raphael 188
Holland family 118
Hooker, John 67, 112, 136
horses 40-41, 77
houses 59-60, 77-8
  prehistoric 65
Hoveden, Roger 136, 145, 185
Hundreds 103
hunting, birds 41
  cattle 40
  deer 38-9
  fox 38
The Hurlers 154
hurling 86-9

Iew family 175
inns 77
Ireland 78, 101
islands 43
John, King 31, 93
John of Cornwall 67
John of Northampton 143
John of Salisbury 98
Julius Caesar 18, 91
Justices of the Peace 104-7

Keckwitch family 126
kelp burning 44
Kendall family 158, 165, 171, 175, 179
Kennal, Dr 64, 69
Kerrier Hundred 179-85
Killigrew family 57, 71, 128, 138, 160,

180-1
Kiltor 73
Kingsand 112
Kingston, Sir Anthony 147-8

Ladock 166
landholding, law and custom 56-9
Land's End 13, 23, 191-2
Langdon family 128
La(n)gherne family 179, 185
Lanine/Lanyon family 21, 184, 185
Lanreath 104
Launcels 139
Launceston 60, 61, 76, 79, 95, 97, 104,
  108, 131, 136-7, 170
  local pronunciation of 136
Lawhitton 136
lawyers 15, 69
Lear, King 91
Lelant 61
leprosy 79-80
Lesnewth Hundred 103-4, 142-6
lestercocks 53-4, 179
Lezant 137
lice 37
lime 18
lip-reading 132
Liskeard 27, 60, 61, 76, 95, 104, 108,
  153
The Lizard 183, 190
Lock family 128, 174
London merchants 28
Loe Pool 183
Looe 43, 60, 104, 108, 152-3
Lord Warden 8, 14, 31-3, 94, 131, 135
Lostwithiel 27, 32, 60, 61, 76, 96, 108,
  162, 164-5
Lower family 73, 101, 106, 138, 157,
  171
Lutterel family 115

Lynher, River 43, 46-7, 116, 125-6,
128-30
Lyonesse 13

Manaton family 138
Marazion (Market Jew) 61, 188, 190
Mark, King 92
markets 34, 60, 76
Marney, Lord 74
Marrow family 179
Mary Rose 72
Matthew Paris 143
Matthew of Westminster 11, 67, 78,
91, 154
May family 158
Medhope family 69
Members of Parliament 108
Meneage 183
Menheniot 60, 79, 138
Merlin 143, 191
Merther 39
Mevagissey 168
Michael Joseph an Gof 111
Michael of Cornwall 68, 99
Milbrook 60, 115-6
Militon family 156, 183, 184
mining, *see* tin extraction
miracle plays 84
Mitchell family 69
Mitchell 108
Mohun family 39, 74, 100, 158-9
Monck family 116, 180
moorstone (granite) 17
Mordred 145
Moreman family 69
Mount Edgcumbe 113-6
Mousehole 188
Moyle family 59, 69, 106, 158
mules 40-41
Murth family 156

Nance family 62, 185
Naphant, Sir John 72
Netherlands 18, 72, 101, 167, 178,
181
Newlyn 189, 191
Newquay (new Kaye) 178-9
Nichols family 69, 151
Notter Bridge 128
nunnery 97

Orgerius, Duke of Cornwall 93, 131
Osbourne family 99
'other-half stone' *see* Doniert
otters 38
oxen 40
Oxford, John Earl of 187
oysters 49, 125-6

Padstow 43, 104, 105, 172
parishes 98 (*see also* feasts)
Parker, Sir Nicholas 99, 100, 106, 183,
184
Parks, Humphrey 99
pastimes 80-90
Paul 188, 191
Payton family 170
pearls 18
Pelynt 60
Pendarves 62
Pendennis 102, 180
Pengersick 184
Penkevil family 151, 171
Penryn 60, 97, 104, 108, 181
Pentewan 151, 168
Pentire 151
Penwarne family 185
Penwith Hundred 185-92
Penzance 60, 101, 104, 188-9, 191
Peranzabuloe 97, 178
physicians 69-70

pilchard 51-3
piracy 162, 182
[hinted at] 76
Plymouth 11-13, 43, 112-5, 135, 179-80, 189
Polidore Vergil 13, 92
Polperro 157
Polruan 159
Polston Bridge 69
Polsue family 74
Polwhele family 171
(de) Pomeroy family 171, 186-7
porpoise 48, 50
portents 21, 159, 168, 173
Porter family 131
ports 43-44
poverty 78-9
Powder Hundred 103-4, 160-171
Power, Sir H 190
Prideaux family 172, 177
priories 97
prisons 79, 108, 130, 137, 141, 164
Probus 60, 97, 168
Ptolemy 62
puffins 55
pumps 23-4
Pydar Hundred 172-79

quarrying 17-18
quoits 22

rabbits 38
Ralegh, Sir Walter (Lord Warden of the Stannaries) 8, 31-2, 57, 73, 95, 99
Rame Head 112, 169
Rashleigh family 162, 171, 183
rats 37
Rattenbury family 99
rebellions, see risings

Rescrowe family 62
Reskymer family 39, 62, 138, 157, 166, 182
Restormel 95, 165
Resuggan family 111
Revenge 72
Richard, Earl of Cornwall 93-4, 143
risings 111-2, 131, 147, 187
rivers 42-3
roads 60, 81
Roche 165-6
Roderic, King of the Britons 92, 109
rogues and vagabonds 78-9
Rolls 69
Romane, John 73
Romans 20, 32, 60, 84, 91, 153
Roscarrock family 151, 171, 179
Roseland 169
Rouse family 39, 100, 131, 133-4
Russell family 99, 131

saints' feasts, see feasts
St Agnes 178
St Aubyn family 128, 166, 174, 182, 183-4
St Buryan 97, 192
St Cleer 153
St Columb 60, 104, 173
St Endellion 150
St Ewe 169
St Germans 61, 96-7, 108, 126-8
St Ives 43, 60, 108, 185
St John family 175
St Keby 67
St Keyne 154-5
St Keverne 111
St Kew 151
St Lawrence (nr Bodmin) 61
St Leger family 139
St Mawes 102, 108, 171, 180

St Michael's Mount 13, 25, 60, 102, 140, 186-8, 190
St Neot 21, 154
St Nunn's Well 146
St Piran 67
St Stephens 61, 136
St Winnow 157
salmon 45-8
Saltash 60, 61, 104, 108, 125, 132-3, 146
sand (for improving land) 44
Sawle family 171
Saxon conquest 11, 109
Sayer family 69
schools 72, 141, 148
Scilly 13, 102, 192
seals 51, 54, 185
Seaton 128
seaweed as a manure 44
seine fishing 48, 51-3
sheep 39
shellfish 44, 48-9
shipbuilding 76
shipping 45
Sidney, Sir Philip 117
silver 18
Skawn 69
skittles 22
Skuish (or Skewes), John 69
slate 17, 18
Sled family 99
snakes 37
smuggling (export) 34
soldiers 72, 98-101
Southcott family 134
Spenser, Edmund 65
springs, see wells
Spurr family 138
Stannaries 30-33, 94
Strabo 62, 109

Stow 139
Stowell family 69
Stratton 60, 104, 139
Stratton Hundred 103-4, 138-42
Stucley, Thomas 135
Sumaster, Thomas 97
swallows, hibernation myth 42

Tamar, River 13, 43, 110, 112
Tanner family 171
Taprel 21
Tehidy 185
Temple 97, 152
three men's songs 84
Thurlebeare family 175
Thurnay, Simon 67
tide mills 43
timber 36
tin, extraction of 19-24, 178, 184
  law and customs 26-7, 30-3
  processing 24-6, 36
tin, economics of trade, 27-30
Tintagel 61, 102, 141-4
towns 65, 76-7, 104-5
Totnes 12, 13, 181
'Tre, Pol and Pen' 62
Trecarrel 137
Tredenham family 177
Tredinnick family 179
Treffry family 69, 99-100, 156, 160-1, 171
Trefusis family 106, 181, 184
Tregian family 115
Tregodeck family 138
Tregonwell, Sir John 71
Tregony 60, 61 108, 170
Tregose family 156
Tregury, Michael 68
Trelawney family 39, 74, 138, 159
Trelowarren 39, 183

Trematon 95, 130-1
Tremayne family 69, 115, 128, 138, 139, 160, 165, 169
Trenance family 105
Trencreek family 171
Trengove family 62, 185
Trenowith, Sir Henry 169
Trenwith family 184
Trerice 175
Trethurffe family 159, 166
Trevanion family 39, 55, 105, 106, 169, 171
Trevilian family 116
Trevisa family 68, 134, 138
Trigg Hundred 103-4, 146-152
'Tristan stone' 163
Trivet, Thomas 69
Truro 27, 60, 76, 97, 105, 106, 108, 170, 181
Tubb family 69, 105
Tywardreath 97, 163

Upton family 157
Ursula, Saint 92
Uther Pendragon 92, 143

Vaughan family 128
Veale, of Bodmin 73, 150
Veale (Vyell) family 137, 172

Vivian family 39, 100, 106, 159, 171, 179, 181, 183
Wadebridge 172
Wadham family 131
wage rates 22
Wales and the Welsh 11, 13, 18, 36, 62-3, 78, 91, 92, 95, 96, 109-10, 136
Walter of Exeter 68
Warbeck, Perkin 111, 147, 187
water power 24
Week St Mary 61, 140-1
weights and measures 61-2
wells 42, 146, 150-1, 154, 173
West Hundred 103-4, 152-60
Wideslade family 111, 157
wild herbs 33-4
William the Bastard [a.k.a. the Conqueror] 93
William of Greenfield 68
William of Malmesbury 109
Williams, John 69
Williams, Thomas 63
wine-making 36
Witchalse family 169
Wolverstone family 180
Wray family 73, 138
wrestling 11-12, 89-90

yeomanry 77